Dear Hans & Karen,

I hope you will enjoy my first book!
It's only just out today. If you like it,
please leave a review at the Amazon
page!

All the best, Matt

Amazon: http://amzn.to/futureisnow

THE FUTURE IS NOW

First published in the United Kingdom by Futurist.Matt Publishing, 2017
Futurist.Matt Publishing is an imprint of ModComms Limited
http://www.futuristmatt.com

For information contact: info@futuristmatt.com

Paperback ISBN 978-0-9957223-0-9
Ebook ISBN 978-0-9957223-1-6

Cover and interior designed by www.modcommslimited.com.

Printed in the UK by Geoff Neal Group.

British Library Cataloguing in Publication Data.
A catalogue record for this book is available from the British Library.

PART I: THE FUTURE OF BUSINESS

LEADERSHIP //40

THE FUTURE OF WORK //54

 # PART II: THE FUTURE OF SOCIETY

CRIME //116

TECHNOLOGY //130

CONCLUSION //150

PREFACE

This is not the place or time for predictions. 'The horse is here to stay, but the automobile is just a novelty' are words reportedly delivered to Henry Ford's lawyer by a bank manager, to discourage him from investing. The truth is that the future doesn't happen to us, but is created by us. Therefore, my aim is to create a set of signposts to the changes that are emerging and offer some considered thought around each one. My belief is that predicting the future is a fool's errand, but my job is to bring structure to a seemingly chaotic world; and we can certainly identify the overwhelming trends, which are changing so many aspects of our lives.

The Future is Now is focused on helping people navigate a fast-changing world. We're not looking at 50, 20 or even 10 years into the future. More often, the changes we explore are affecting us now and my interest is in what they might mean in a mere 5 to 10 years as this is the reality that we are working with, in business and society at large. The trends developing currently are non-linear; they are often enmeshed into our lives in ways that it is almost impossible to untangle. This intricacy and overlap is visualised here through imagery, diagrams and media content, designed to stimulate your thinking and allow you to pursue areas of particular interest further. Delving in and out of each topic offers the opportunity to see the synergies and complexities of these changes, as well as the potential positive and negative impacts.

It is increasingly apparent that the combination of a VUCA (Volatile, Uncertain, Complex and Ambiguous) world and the pressure to deliver virtually instant results forces a constant burden on our leaders. As markets become more transparent, the impetus for firms to differentiate grows. This extends into branding and developing new products and services as customer buying patterns become more sophisticated. Western businesses urgently need to demonstrate why their offerings are worth a premium price compared to those with lower operating costs in China, India, Vietnam and the Philippines.

Since beginning my journey as a futurist, working alongside businesses that are facing this reality, i've become incredibly optimistic about the power of innovation to solve so many of our challenges. The future may be coming upon us scarily and quickly, but the revolution it is bringing can be a positive one, economically, environmentally and societally if we learn how to spot and to embrace the trends that will work for us. Whether it be adopting new leadership styles, embracing the 'gig' economy, investing in virtual reality or artificial intelligence, or embracing the power of the people in the digital environment – this is the time to not just watch change happen but become part of it and drive it to where you and your company need to be.

INTRODUCTION

We are entering a world of accelerated change, one fuelled by idea sharing on a scale that could never have been dreamt of even 10 years ago. As Generation 'Z' (typically those born in the mid-1990s onwards) is introduced to the working world, they arrive as people who haven't even known a world without social networks. As such, collaboration is the norm, not the exception.

Ventures are crowdfunded – think Kickstarter or the success of microloans in developing nations. Marketers seek advice from their customers, either overtly in the form of designing your own jeans or mobile phone packages and holidays, or covertly if you only imagine all that browsing data you give away every day. We are all constantly finding new ways to collaborate and organise society and business.

Although all this pooling of ideas and creativity is fun for most, some trends can be uncomfortable, because they disrupt the status quo and the comfort of 'This is how we've always done it'. Take, for example, the many effects of digitisation and the Cloud on photography. The once legendary Kodak went spectacularly bankrupt and feels as sepia-tinted today as its finest film. Yet another film brand, Polaroid, has thrived in the digital era, with new devices and niches, including micro-printers for the most visual of all the social networks, Instagram. Underpinning them all is the Cloud-based storage of our photos. Never mind ancient albums, our children will look at our hard drives and wonder what on earth we were thinking of. All that hardware, and restricted to just 256GB. Perhaps the very definition of 'disruption' is to look back five years and think 'I can't believe we used to...' Disruption challenges our world-views, and – since many of us spend more time connected and at work than anywhere else – our very identities.

Tech evangelists love to talk about how the world is getting smaller, with virtual and physical borders breaking down, but 2017 makes us question whether this is truly the case. In the US, we see Donald Trump ascending to the presidency by trouncing his opposition using divisive language devoid of substance. Closer to home, the UK voted to leave the European

Union in a landmark referendum. Are the emerging political trends at odds with the technical trends born of Silicon Valley? While technology seeks to break down barriers, the current political mood seems intent on building them up.

Today, as our cities expand and we routinely cheat death with medicine, we are engaged in a race between our lifestyles and our ability to manage the natural resources at our disposal. Whoever said 'necessity is the mother of invention' deserves great credit – we are on the cusp of some of the most challenging, and therefore inventive, times in human evolution. Everyone needs to re-appropriate the ideas that work for them.

Indeed, ideas are truly the only resource that expands rather than depletes the more we use it. Ideas are like DNA: they are copied and refined and mutate over time. Those with value stick while those without, wither away. Take the wheel – it was not a policy decision that helped the invention spread. It was simply copied and proven in the harsh test bed of trial and error.

The Future is Now is deliberately diverse in its range of topics. There's significant crossover between sections as they are inextricably linked together. To give just one example, while Artificial Intelligence is covered in its own right, there's little doubt it will become pervasive across society and business more widely. Not only are many of us carrying super computers in our pockets, these also include voice activated 'AI' assistants in the form of Apple's Siri, Google's Now and Microsoft's Cortana.

We need to remain open-minded to thrive in the new world. As technology increasingly merges with our everyday lives, it's important to use it rather than be used by it. Current agricultural and manufacturing methods are often harmful to the environment, but we shouldn't abstain from them completely. Instead, we should look towards new fuels such as algae oil and cultured meat; both of which are covered later on. On a spiritual level, we will come to understand our own 'operating systems' as outlined in 'Human Doing to Human Being.' Through a better understanding of the 'self,' we will find ourselves to be more resourceful, resilient and creative than ever before.

⚙ BUSINESS

As the difference between private and public sectors blur across the developed world, commerce is becoming a greater part of our lives. Trade is why 19% of the global population lacked sufficient food in 1992, but has fallen to 11% in 2016. Businesses are also the source of many good ideas: they have budgets to fund innovation and they also have an incentive in the profit motive. Not only is innovation essential to competition, but many people believe we're on the cusp of a new kind of commerce altogether.

As our exposure to advertising becomes saturated, as people rebel against consumerism and as experiences like virtual reality (VR) step-change the media, products and services are on an accelerated path to a brave new world.

In 'From More to Better,' we see how progressive organisations are recognising that it's good business sense to adopt a multi-stakeholder approach when measuring their success. New leaders arrive with new values and are seeking to instil more purpose in what their organisations do. This approach is being more formally enshrined in Benefit Corporations – companies designed from scratch to create profit, but also with strong social and environmental visions.

And we see how transparency forces organisations to stay at the top of their game in order to keep customers happy.

In 'From the Mass to the Personal,' we begin to explore how new technology facilitates greater product personalisation. It can be a profitable strategy, as proven by the 'Share a Coke' campaign of 2014. Furthermore, 3D printing will enable everything from replacement parts for products and customised consumer goods right through to new body parts.

Organisations with a mission and which inspire and facilitate our lifestyles are set to win in years to come.

FROM MORE
TO BETTER

How commercial entities will
play a greater role in society
and be judged on more than
just market performance

From More to Better

For at least two decades, large organisations have been slaves to consumerism and the demands of their shareholders. As markets have rightly become more transparent, shareholder value has been perceived in ever more short-term demands for gain and profit – often quarter by quarter – at the expense of long-term planning and strategy. The only way to satisfy those demands has been to sell more stuff and make more money. This has led to enormous organisations that are unable to respond swiftly to rapidly changing market conditions.

Let's look at where this has happened:

COMPANY	YEAR WENT BUST	DESTROYER	CAUSE OF DOWNFALL
BORDERS	2011	AMAZON	• Too late to digital • Didn't embrace e-books • Opened stores as consumers move online
KODAK	2012	MOBILE PHONES	• Failed to prepare for its own disruption • Dabbled in its own development
MINITEL	2012	WORLD WIDE WEB	• Kept their system closed while the web was open • Access terminals proprietary and not released widely enough
PHILIPS CONSUMER ELECTRONICS	2013	SAMSUNG	• Laid back investment approach

In the world of better, success is measured not only against traditional quantitative metrics (sales; earnings before interest, taxes, depreciation and amortisation (EBITDA) etc) but on qualitative goodwill: being a fulfilling place to work, developing innovation and originality, contributing to education and making an on-the-ground difference to the communities in which a business has a presence.

Sir Andrew Witty,
Outgoing CEO, GSK.
Source: **GSK Corporate**

Take the pharmaceutical giant, GSK, for example. In December 2016, it was reported that the 'Access to Medicines Foundation' had placed them top of their league table, in part because of the leadership of outgoing CEO, Andrew Witty. He slashed prices in their poorest markets early on and instigated new intellectual property (IP) arrangements to facilitate

greater generic production. While still accountable to shareholders, GSK has led the way in reversing the perception that Big Pharma is the problem in global healthcare and not the solution.

But as we approach the peak of consumerism at the same time as geopolitical unrest and financial inequality make themselves felt across the globe, smart businesses are coming to realise that a new approach is required to sustain business operations and keep customers happy.

That's why Mark Benioff, the Chairman and CEO of world-leading customer relationship management (CRM) and sales venture, Salesforce.com has joined seasoned business leaders like General Electric's ex-Chairman Jack Welch and Alibaba's Jack Ma in saying: '*The business of business isn't just about creating profits for shareholders – it's also about improving the state of the world and driving stakeholder value.*'

Having or buying more stuff is no longer making people happy – and that is not a recipe for good business. Instead of growing larger, enterprises will

Ben and Jerry's: The B-Corp: futuristmatt.com/fonlinks

find they are better at pursuing both the goals of their business, their investors and their customers if they become smaller, more agile and more connected. They will benefit from engaging with their customers, producing better products (which can often yield higher returns), and discovering their social conscience along with product delivery.

In the US, a whole category of Benefit Corporations (or 'B Corps') has emerged which leverage the power of business architecture to solve social and environmental problems as well as delivering goods. The poster child for B Corp practice is Unilever-owned ice cream-maker, Ben and Jerry's. Paying fair wages, buying responsibly and conducting 'social audits' has paid off. It's created fiercely loyal customers prepared to pay for a premium product. All of this has made it one of Unilever's most profitable brands.

Travel on most airlines, and you'll hear the hackneyed, but true, announcement: 'Thank you for flying with us: we always remember that you have a choice.'

The transparency delivered by online marketplaces and user-generated review sites such as TripAdvisor means that consumers do have total choice; and the prevalence of review information means that products that are second-rate or represent bad value will soon be found out.

Better products, better for the world around us.

Video: 'Miguel Veiga-Pestana on the sustainability agenda at Unilever and purpose driven business'.

See futuristmatt.com/fonvideos
Hybrid book users: Video 4

FROM THE MASS
TO THE PERSONAL

How customisation is replacing economies of scale as a driver of profitability

Open Hand Project: futuristmatt.com/fonlinks

From the Mass to the Personal

Personalisation isn't new. I can remember the day my mum gifted me a 'Me and Mayor Stubbs' book. It was something about a rabbit collecting Easter eggs. The detail escapes me, but I still remember after 32 years that 'Matt' was a central character. I was the story. But product personalisation is being taken to new levels, with both positive and negative effects.

The Industrial Revolution of the nineteenth century unlocked a period of mass manufacture, characterised by assembly lines, job and batch production. Today, we have entered the age of mass customisation, where computer-aided manufacturing systems can create personalised output.

You may remember the 'Share a Coke' campaign from 2014 when Coca-Cola printed over 1,000 different names on their plastic bottles. Not only did this campaign generate 235,000 tweets using the hashtag #shareacoke, but it also saw 730,000 glass bottles personalised via their e-com-merce store. During the campaign, Coca-Cola saw a 2% lift in sales while competitors, including Snapple and PepsiCo, saw negative growth. The campaign not only lifted sales, but it also saw customers doing the marketing themselves. A true win-win situation for Coca-Cola!

There's no single trend narrative for customisation and personalisation, and no single hard and fast way to analyse it. You can build your own car, create a bespoke holiday, and design your own jeans. Oh, and for US $150, you can design a replacement hand!

Very soon you'll be able to regrow a range of body parts including a heart, liver and kidneys! Alongside these advances, there will no doubt be increasingly complex ethical issues. On a less fundamental scale but important nonetheless, 3D printing will soon allow us to print replacement parts for consumer goods cheaply: repairs on our terms. It's also a bonus for the environment as consumers produce exactly what they need rather than according to supplier forecasts.

These examples represent a range of benefits and problems. Regrowing a heart is, most would agree, unconditionally good. As 3D printing becomes ubiquitous, moving first to the high street and then into our homes, there's a good argument that 'the means of production' – to quote the old socialist phrase – is democratised back to the individual; effectively reversing some of the centralisation that began with the Industrial Revolution.

Equally, this is a new consumer battleground. We will be less defined by what we buy and more defined by how we live. The future of commerce belongs to those organisations that best inspire and facilitate our

lifestyles. On the one hand, that may see us being less wasteful, driving economies out of a customised supply chain. But equally we may add to the twenty-first century's problem with waste, buying things that are unique and therefore more ephemeral.

The solution lies in the advancement of materials science and their associated recycling/reuse which will render waste a non-issue anyway.

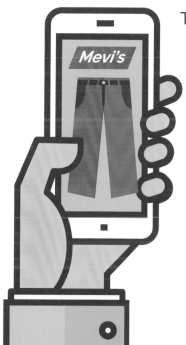

The days of 'Made and Crafted by Levi's' are on the way out and a new era of 'Made by Me' is on the way in!

⚏ MANUFACTURING

In 'Supply Chains to Supply Networks', we explore how supply chains are morphing in response to volatility and changing consumer demand. One answer to this is the way supply chains are moving towards 'supply networks', increasing the opportunity to hedge their financial and delivery options.

New technologies are set to reduce cost and increase efficiency throughout the supply chain, all of which we explore in 'New Business Models and Technology.'

In 'The Factory of the Future', we look at the evolution of industry through multiple revolutions – from Industry 1.0, the original birth of specialisation and technology to today's Industry 4.0. There's no doubt new materials will influence new products too, so we explore so-called '2D' graphene and examine just one example of how it's being used right now. A key driver for factories going forward is the increased use of data resulting from sensors, from production processes to the logistics of finished products and back

to the factory again. As the pressure on cultivatable land continues to grow, agriculture goes indoors, multi-storey and largely autonomous. In addition, we see how small manufacturers can be competitive and profitable through the smart use of new technologies, employing lessons learned from so called 'Pilot Fabs' – fully working models aimed at testing innovative production methods. Keeping it all going are Enterprise Resource Planning (ERP) systems, and trends like the Internet of Things, wearable technology and Big Data analytics are all set to drive the evolution of and value from ERP. But with this wave of data, we need more data scientists to create insight from information.

The future of manufacturing is certainly an exciting one.

SUPPLY CHAINS TO SUPPLY NETWORKS

How complexity and risk are being reduced in the connected supply chain

Supply Chains to Supply Networks

What used to be the supply chain is increasingly the supply network. This is the inevitable result of the challenges facing today's global supply chains. Breaks in the chain are usually resolved quickly.

Take the example of the volcanic ash over Iceland in 2010. Global production was unusually unaffected. However, just one year later when the Tōhoku earthquake struck Japan, things weren't quite so smooth. Both HP computers and General Motors suffered as a result of factory shutdowns at the time. It's unlikely to have affected Apple's production too much as industry experts estimate just one third of its memory chips come from Japan with two thirds from South Korea – hence demonstrating the resilience of the network. As organisations seek to grow and expand into new markets, they have to look at whether existing supply chains are capable of servicing these objectives. There will be fads to contend with as well. Take Paleo energy bars for example. This product exists in the highly regulated food industry, yet wasn't available before 2010. In both 2013/14, demand surged suddenly – almost certainly as a result of increased US media coverage.

Supply chains have never been so volatile, which leads to permanent uncertainty. Customer loyalty is lower than ever as market transparency and price sensitivity increase. Complex global supply chains render products sensitive to geopolitical upheaval. According to a 2013 study by PricewaterhouseCoopers (PwC), 75% of survey respondents considered volatility and poor forecast accuracy to be the biggest challenge they faced. The same study found that participants felt their new growth would come from international customers and customised products.

Video: 'Professor James Woudhuysen on Geopolitics and Supply Networks.'

See futuristmatt.com/fonvideos
Hybrid book users: Video 5

It's no coincidence that Starbucks plan to open a further 3400 stores in China by 2019 (on top of the 2,100 spread across 102 cities in 2016). No doubt this impressive growth is linked to the fact that customers can order 'Venti Iced Skinny Hazelnut Macchiato, Sugar-Free Syrup, Extra Shot, Light Ice, No Whip coffee,' if that's what they want! You don't get a product much more customised than that.

2016

2019

2100 Stores

3400 Stores

Customers are more aware and connected than ever. To meet this challenge, companies need 'Digital Supply Networks' which are more than simply physical networks, but rather encompass broader business parameters: information, talent and finance. This is especially true for manufacturing as it moves away from shifting product and towards offering services – so-called 'servitisation'.

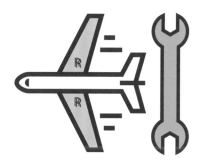

For example, you don't buy jet engines from Rolls Royce anymore. You buy $ per engine flying hour. If the service level agreement stipulates a designated percentage of uptime, you had better have engineers available to maintain the engines – wherever that happens to be.

The demand in China for Starbucks is mirrored more generally by global trade, which is anticipated to rise by the World Bank to US $27 trillion by 2030. That's approaching double the US $16.5 trillion of merchandise trade recorded by the World Trade Organisation (WTO) in 2015. To maintain these trade flows, we will be forced to innovate. Manpower Group stated in 2015 that finding drivers was one of the top ten jobs that were hardest to fill in the US. This could be solved by the use of driverless trucks as the infrastructure to support them increases, but we'll cover this later.

NEW BUSINESS MODELS AND TECHNOLOGY

How the availability of data is powering disintemediation, servitisation and other new business models

New Business Models and Technology

Existing supply models are being disrupted on a worldwide basis. With the arrival of the web came 'disintermediation' – a watchword for the removal of middlemen (dealers, wholesalers, advisors, representatives, agents, etc.) – facilitating producers being able to sell directly to consumers. The theory was that manufacturers could receive a larger share of revenues while prices to consumers dropped. It didn't work out that way. A new breed of stronger intermediaries was born, and manufacturers were forced to reduce costs as these new distributors controlled access to the markets. That said, some fought back...

Examples of the manufacturers taking charge include Dell and Tesla. Dell pioneered a highly successful model where they sold their computers directly to customers online. Elon Musk's electric car producer, Tesla, offers direct sales of their vehicles via their own website. Indeed, high-tech product manufacturers are often united by their use of a hybrid model – online and traditional channels.

Retailers used to work with wholesalers as they handled the complex task of paying the thousands of suppliers that big retailers depended on. US retail giant, Walmart, dispensed with wholesalers by clever use of internet and computer technologies to handle their own wholesaling functions. This reduced prices for consumers and facilitated their growth to turn over US $488 billion in 2015 – a 2% increase on 2014.

Amazon moved away from the traditional retail model completely. Not only do they sell almost anything, but it's done entirely online and through their new 'Echo' voice activated device. Apple is a little different as they pay factories they don't own to produce their products. It's a model that works well for them, especially as they include direct retail sales in their channel mix. All of these approaches reduce the power of the actual producers.

Amazon Echo includes '**Alexa**', a personal assistant, who performs tasks and controls various systems within the home.

My sense is this is just the beginning. The Echo represents Amazon's bid to become the operating system of our homes.

Amazon Prime Air: futuristmatt.com/fonlinks

Expect to see far greater use of new technologies such as Radio Frequency Identification (RFID) tags by the already highly profitable companies active in the distribution space. Their tracking will be integral in the use of new tools like drones, driverless trucks and automated warehouses. There is also likely to be an increase in the use of automation technology such as 'Pick/Pack' robots, which in combination can lead to total automation.

Business owners won't even require inventory lists because they'll know exactly what's in a warehouse at any moment. Right now, the issues aren't with the storage of items, but the picking. While robots can already distinguish items of varying shapes and even pick up what's required, they're still significantly slower at doing so than their human counterparts. Once the picking issue is solved, fully automated warehouses will become the norm. You may remember the publicity around Amazon's drone delivery video a few years ago. Many of us thought it was the beginning of a new era. However, the real challenge isn't in the delivery (though getting drones to deliver to your door when you live in an apartment block could be tricky). It's in creating a reliable system that makes financial sense and doesn't contravene ever-increasing regulations. In July 2016, the UK Civil Aviation Authority granted special dispensation for Amazon to begin the testing of delivery drones in a rural area near Cambridge. Indeed, their first ever trial customer delivery took place in December 2016. The interesting thing here isn't the technology, but how the airspace regulator is open to what's possible.

Amazon Prime Air – First Customer Delivery, December 7 2016, UK
See futuristmatt.com/fonvideos
Hybrid book users: Video 6

Even once the legal issues are resolved, it's still necessary to get the economics right. At the moment, trucks are a far lower cost for heavy loads or goods needing delivery over 100km. It's the 'final mile' for shorter distances and lighter deliveries where drones could come into their own. In part, that's because of battery life. Current drones are estimated to be capable of carrying around 10kg up to 14km range before requiring recharging. If charge points are only at the point of origin, that range is halved, as they'll need to return to base.

It's anticipated that customers would use landing pads, which would require placing on a flat area in order to receive deliveries. Drones would pick up from local depots, drop the goods and move on to their next destination. These depots could be centralised warehouses or even local supermarkets. Stranger yet, another idea is that delivery vans could release swarms of drones for concurrent deliveries, then move to another district to repeat the process. It would certainly increase the number of deliveries a truck could make in a day – as well as minimising the human interventions required and number of errors.

We've seen recently that Uber are experimenting with self-driving cars in the US and trucks that drive themselves might not be far away. Getting these right will be extremely complex, as driving conditions will vary wildly and include often complex endpoints for customers. Driverless trucks will be more straightforward to develop as they can easily move along motorways and other major roads to staging areas specifically designed for them. Combine these with drones and automated warehouses, and we're heading towards a completely automatic supply chain – at least, up to that tricky 'final mile.' Components and fully formed products will move 365 days a year from suppliers to factories to end customers.

In the scenario of customer houses being on the trunk routes, delivery drones could even make the 'final mile' of the delivery route while the automated trucks are heading to local depots.

Mercedes Self-Driving Trucks: futuristmatt.com/fonlinks

These autonomous trucks would know what's on-board by checking RFID tags, while customers would have precise knowledge of where their products are at any time of day. For added efficiency, these automated trucks could easily run at quieter times, during holidays and even operate through the night without taking breaks.

In summary, the traceability of individual products through RFID tags, bulk transportation of automated trucks and possibilities of delivery drones for the 'final mile' will certainly make the supply networks of the future operate more predictably and quickly.

It's clear that the new business models caused by a disruption in supply chains will be a good thing, increasing efficiencies and hopefully passing on lower costs to consumers.

THE FACTORY OF THE FUTURE

How new materials, production processes and evolving consumer demand are driving change in manufacturing

The Factory of the Future

As with all new trends, the factory of the future is represented by different themes for different people. Read the industry press, and you'll see terms like 'Industry 4.0' and 'Smart Manufacturing' bandied about like jelly beans. I think it describes how new technologies are creating change in manufacturing on a par with how water- and steam-powered mechanical manufacturing ushered in the first industrial revolution at the end of the eighteenth century. It's not all IT-driven or virtual, either. New materials, production processes and consumer demand models are all serving to drive disruption. Every production process requires raw materials, so let's look at just one example.

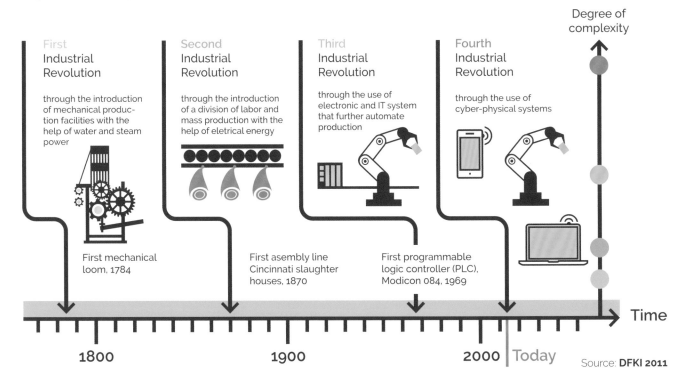

First
Industrial
Revolution

through the introduction of mechanical production facilities with the help of water and steam power

Second
Industrial
Revolution

through the introduction of a division of labor and mass production with the help of eletrical energy

Third
Industrial
Revolution

through the use of electronic and IT system that further automate production

Fourth
Industrial
Revolution

through the use of cyber-physical systems

Degree of complexity

First mechanical loom, 1784

First asembly line Cincinnati slaughter houses, 1870

First programmable logic controller (PLC), Modicon 084, 1969

Time

1800   1900   2000 | Today

Source: **DFKI 2011**

Momo Design: futuristmatt.com/fonlinks

Graphene has been widely discussed since its discovery in 2004. If you've ever drawn with a pencil, you've created it yourself. It's considered to be a '2d' material in that it's only a single atom thick. What makes it so interesting for manufacturers is that it's super strong, ultra light, super conductive and thus offers a multitude of potential uses. Applications include water purification, wearable technology, lightweight aircraft and electric cars. Some scientists refer to it as the 'miracle material' and suggest that it will change almost every industry.

Graphene is set to save lives and make you look good while doing it. In November 2016, the Italian motorcycle helmets company, Momodesign, partnered with Italian graphene producer, IIT, to implement a new graphene-coated helmet product. Not only are these helmets considered to offer better protection in the event of an impact, but they can also be made thinner than conventional helmets. Furthermore, their heat resistant qualities are expected to reduce the damage associated with the use of helmets in hot countries where high temperatures can negatively affect their structural integrity.

Youll notice how thin the shell is compared to conventional helmets.
Credit: **MOMO Design**

Materials aside, the greatest driver for change in manufacturing is how both internal and external processes are being moulded by access to data. This could be through a single platform, but now that systems integration and application programming interfaces (APIs) are commonplace, this is more likely to be a se-

IIT Graphene Labs: futuristmatt.com/fonlinks

ries of interconnected modules that can easily share and make sense of information. The scope for useful collaboration between customers, product designers and production personnel is enormous. With robots to assist production, defect levels will drop. All this, coupled with the on-demand availability of materials, will afford the production of massively personalised products, right first time and fit for customer purpose.

Information has to come from somewhere. Data once came from men (and it usually was men) with clipboards; today it's from a wide array of sensors. The Industrial Internet of Things (IIot) is predicated on the fact that we can get increased information from a higher number of sensors, more widely distributed across a supply chain or production line, delivered in real time to more devices and processing power than ever. We don't even need to look to industrial technology to source data: mobile phones, for example, now have a dazzling array of sensors; everything from GPS (location), accelerometers (tilt), temperature and humidity. Indeed, following the Fukushima earthquake and resulting nuclear disaster, Sharp introduced the 'Pantone 5' phone with a built-in Geiger counter. These

low-cost sensors facilitate data collection both during a production process and long after. Motorcycle manufacturer, Harley-Davidson, increased the uptime of their Pennsylvania facility by constantly monitoring their production processes. If a machine reports an out-of-range parameter, it's adjusted remotely to avoid malfunction. This preventative, rather than remedial, monitoring cuts out huge amounts of downtime. GE, Siemens and Cisco all operate similar systems.

As you might expect, some of the most automated manufacturing comes out of China. In 2015, it was estimated that 75,000 multipurpose robots were in use on production lines in China. The International Federation of Robotics expects that number to double by the end of 2018. In mid-2016, it was widely reported that electronics manufacturer Foxconn had cut its human workforce by 60,000, but had maintained production capacity thanks to a massive investment in robots. It's easy to proselytise on manufacturing job losses, but I see a different trend emerging in the developed world. Step forward 'Cobots.' These are robots developed specifically to assist rather than replace workers. 'Baxter' is one such low-cost example.

Baxter with friend at work

He comes with an SDK (development kit) so manufacturers can programme him for the task in hand. He's best suited to tasks involving danger, lifting or which require precision. At Eurodrive in Baden-Württemberg, Germany, 'Baxter' handles the heavy lifting. Workers report being happier: they certainly get fewer back injuries, but they also take greater pride in their work as they assume more responsibility for the whole production process rather than a single element. It's a good example of robots taking a simple role which allows humans to rise to more complex challenges.

Rethink Robotics: futuristmatt.com/fonlinks

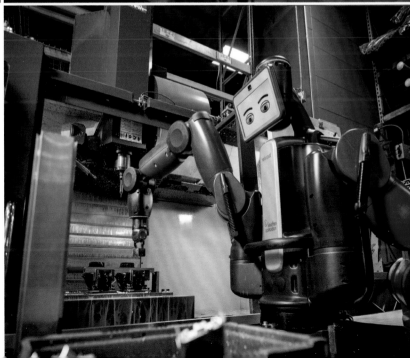

Spread Agri-Factory: futuristmatt.com/fonlinks

Although agriculture is traditionally associated with fields and greenhouses, it is beginning to become more factory-like. As the pressure on cultivatable land grows, we need to expand our thinking about food production. By mid-2017, we can expect to see the first near-autonomous agri-factory open in Kyoto. 'Spread' is expected to produce 30,000 lettuce heads per day. One thing that makes it unusual is that the growing beds are vertically stacked, meaning the output per square foot is significantly higher than simply growing at ground level. LED lights initiate photosynthesis, which requires 30% less energy than current methods and 98% of the water is recycled back into production. By monitoring the photosynthesis, conditions are adjusted throughout the growth process, making production 250% quicker than conventional high-intensity farming. It is worth noting that humans are still required to plant seedlings and confirm germination, so not completely automated quite yet but not far off.

My sense is that it will be a while before we see completely automated factories. Humans and robots will continue to play to their respective strengths. But there is plenty of effort and money going into

Water Filtration System: **98% Recycling Rate**

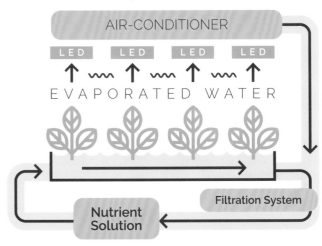

Diagram above highlighting the grow process at the Keihanna techno farm

researching the innovation of automation. For example, we're seeing the growth of 'Pilot Fabs' – low-throughput factories using cutting edge production machines. They allow manufacturers to test techniques before rolling them out and making major balance sheet commitments. Austria doesn't immediately spring to mind when you think of manufacturing, but the Austrian Ministry for Transport, Innovation and Technology has invested €80 million in developing such initiatives. €50 million of that investment will be spent on a new research centre – all to advance the state of manufacturing in the country.

As new technologies and processes come on-stream, we can expect to see manufacturers being more nimble and efficient through better use of software. Step forward Bombsheller, a US firm manufacturing 'graphic leggings'. An artist community provides the designs. These are rendered into 3D realistic images of the finished product. Customers choose the product they want and, only at that point, are the designs printed onto the material. An on-site seamstress then stitches the fabric to shape for the customer.

This 'made to order' approach means the firm spends nothing on demos and never holds large inventories in its own warehouse or with retailers, which might otherwise end up in clearance sales. As 'self-driving sewing machines' such as Sewbo overcome the challenge of robots handling fabrics, it's entirely possible that the clothing production process could become fully automated.

Through a comprehensive use of software across the production process, businesses like Bombsheller challenge the preconception that producing clothing involves bulk ordering of materials and cheap labour; and that economies of scale can only come from mass production. Through designs coming from an online community to manufacture taking place on-site, the production cycle is reduced from what would be months to just days – while personalisation and customisation are embedded as standard.

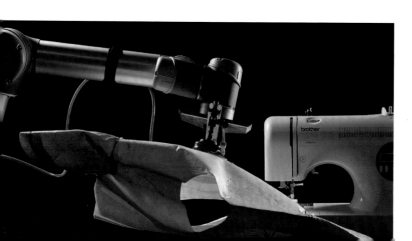

By temporarily stiffening fabrics, 'Sewbo' marks a step change in automating garment manufacturing. Credit: **www.sewbo.com**

Expect to see more near or reshoring of manufacturing in the coming years.

International Data Corporation: futuristmatt.com/fonlinks

As production costs rise in The East, so we are seeing an increase in near or reshoring – repatriating production work back to the developed world. Bombsheller demonstrates how new software and manufacturing techniques can make small garment manufacturers both efficient and profitable. It is also interesting to note that the Bombsheller example suggests how the playing field between large and small manufacturers could become more level. Larger firms are bulk players, refining their lean manufacturing processes; the smaller firms are scaling up by taking advantage of emerging technologies and trends.

We've looked at some of the physical processes shaping manufacturing. However, it's Enterprise Resource Planning (ERP) systems that monitor and manage the whole supply chain, providing visibility to manufacturers around their business processes. At least, that's always been the promise. Like all major software implementations, it has the capacity to be either a silver bullet or a millstone around the neck but usually ends up being something in between. It can facilitate data-driven re-engineering of business processes. Equally, it can come at a high financial and human cost.

Areas ripe for disruption in the future of ERP systems include the IIoT, wearable technologies and Big Data analytics. By 2020, research firm International Data Corporation (IDC) predicts that 40% of data generated globally will come from machines. Further predictions estimate that this flood of digits will emerge from 20 – 50 billion connected devices. Pirelli, the tyre manufacturer, already offers 'smart tyres' with sensors installed. These not only inform drivers and the on-board computer about friction and suspension loads but also give Pirelli real-time information about likely demand levels. The increase in cheap sensors will open up huge opportunities for ERP going forward, as every aspect of a production system is measured and optimised.

Pirelli smart tyres: futuristmatt.com/fonlinks

You'll no doubt be at least familiar with consumer-facing wearable technology like Nike's Fitbit, which converts movements into usable data. It's likely that we'll see more wearable technologies entering manufacturing.

61 BPM

There have been early experiments, including Plex which uses Google Glass. It's been quietly down-played since Google dropped the Glass initiative, but opportunity abounds nonetheless. Expect to see increased use of body cameras to monitor safety and efficiency in production areas. Smart watches are an unobtrusive and easy-to-carry medium to check off production processes and even stop/start the processes themselves. The use of Near Field Com-munication (NFC) sensors could eliminate the need for scanning inventories altogether. Doing so reduces errors and increases efficiency.

My sense is we'll see a mix of body cameras, watches, NFC and other sensors, all feeding into ERP systems to provide better, real-time data to management.

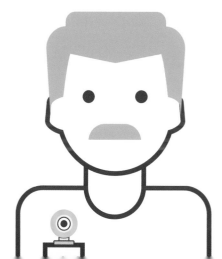

More data doesn't necessarily mean better decisions, though. As we see more integration of ERP and Big Data, we won't refer to Big Data as such anymore – it's all just data. But it's sometimes said that 'we're drowning in data, but starving in insights.' In 2013, the science journal, Nature, reported that Google Flu Trends had overestimated the rise of influenza by 50%. It's thought this was down the dataset itself – just using simple search phrases.

While some jobs are being eroded by technology, one that certainly isn't is that of the data scientist. Making sense of all the information generated by sensors at every stage of a manufacturing process will be increasingly critical. Some speculate that data scientists themselves will be redundant in 10–20 years from now as artificial intelligence takes hold, but I feel we shouldn't ignore the over-riding human factor – critical thinking. It's something machines just can't handle well. Knowing which data points to correlate and which to ignore will be critical to ERP systems and the organisations they serve.

In summary, factories of the future will absolutely exhibit some or all of the following:

- Far more data-driven decision-making based on real-time information
- Software systems will be cloud-based, with greater interoperability between modules from multiple suppliers
- Products will be substantially more personalised – allowing customers greater specificity over features
- Ideas for new product development will come from real-time customer usage through in-built sensors

Constant pressure to become more efficient could be the difference between success and failure for many manufacturers. My sense is that new technologies and materials will see manufacturing work in a similar way to software. Products will be more easily updatable, and preferences accounted for on a case-by-case basis. We will also see shorter supply chains as raw materials are increasingly 'grown' rather than extracted.

These are interesting times indeed.

☷ LEADERSHIP

As we saw in the manufacturing section, supply networks and factories are becoming more complex places. A major driver for this is the amount of data being created and interpreted to inform decisions and new processes. After all, data – when made interpretable – is information, and information is what leaders make decisions on.

In 'Leadership to Followership,' we look at how free information flows were instrumental in bringing about the Arab Spring of 2011. The Arab Spring was also a great example of the effectiveness of distributed leadership. Forward-thinking corporate leaders are sharing the burden too. Ex-Deutsche Bank MD, John Stepper, used an internal online network to crowd-source solutions to business problems.

In 'Analysis to Synthesis,' we look at how brute force analytics are giving way to a mindset more capable of stringing together ideas and making more instinctive decisions.

And in 'Human Doing to Human Being,' we explore an evolving understanding of 'the self' and how leaders of the future will tap into previously unknown resilience, creativity and resourcefulness. Neuroscience is meeting with spirituality and mysticism to reveal that we are already perfectly equipped to handle challenges.

It simply requires a new way of understanding the human 'operating system.'

LEADERSHIP TO FOLLOWERSHIP

How smart leaders are
having their legitimacy
conferred and validated
by their constituencies

Leadership to Followership

The Queen may be a model of serenity and dignity in a changing world, but she is also a model of an older style of leadership which is dying out; legitimacy conferred automatically. Future leaders, whether governmental or corporate, will remain in positions of authority specifically because people are prepared to follow them. Simply having 'manager' on your LinkedIn profile or business card, having a respected qualification, or having epaulettes on your uniform will not be enough: modern leadership is conferred by the crowd, and it is socially validated.

A great example is the movement in Egypt that toppled the former president, Hosni Mubarak. In the uprisings that became known as the Arab Spring, media

interviews on the streets made it clear that nobody was directing the situation. Young people used online tools to force regime change; Mubarak's leadership was devalued by consensus and leadership was instead distributed across the network. They were not the first generation to want him out, but they were the first with the tools and collective mindset to make it happen. Today, Egypt is still in upheaval, and few would say the Arab Spring has achieved either stability or an ideal result in their country, but it is a powerful example of legitimacy being removed by the people.

Man carrying placard during 2011 Egyptian protests demonstrates vital role that social media played.
© Essam Sharaf 2011

John Stepper,
www.workingoutloud.com.

This might seem frightening to some leaders – after all, they fought hard to achieve their hegemony, with long days and plenty of sacrifices along the way. Are they not entitled to their positions? Well, entitlement is exactly the commodity that is being removed. Leaders will be judged on the current environment, not yesterday's effort. They must also carefully manage the 'court of public opinion' on social media – it is more powerful than they are. Transparency is the new norm, and those who lie will be found out.

This challenging world can be softened. To do so, leaders must lose their autocracy and isolation. Smart leaders will 'work out loud,' talking about their work and challenges publicly, online. John Stepper, former MD of Deutsche Bank, for example, introduced 'MyDB'; a company-wide social media platform. He used it to crowdsource solutions to problems and blogged regularly. He was visible, led by example and openly rather than behind closed doors. Leaders may have lost their natural entitlement, but they have gained the opportunity to wield broader influence, with a collaborative justification which can be much harder to unseat.

In the same vein, there is little room for 'heroic' leaders – well-meaning over-achievers like Steve Jobs who predicted and controlled but took the whole world on his shoulders. Some attribute the failure of NeXT computers to his micro-managing approach. After this, he learned to let go more with Pixar, which was a resounding success. Apple's revival was in part down to delegating important duties to his inner circle including Jony Ive and Tim Cook.

But even these heroes are no match for an aligned organisation and a collaborative effort. A future made up of complex and sometimes chaotic environments is simply less suited to lone managers and better suited to smart and flexible networks.

Future leaders will need to instil belief in those that follow them and bring some of those followers up to the top table too.

ANALYSIS TO SYNTHESIS

How the explosion in data puts new value on judgement skills and, perhaps counterintuitively, instinct

Analysis to Synthesis

It is impossible to summarise the great qualities of leadership in a chapter – it's the sort of thing that whole books are written about. But what is interesting is that these qualities are not set in stone. It certainly helps to be committed, to be a great communicator and persuader. But it is also a leader's obligation to be attuned to the world around them and to have enough of an ear to the ground to be able to anticipate change and then react accordingly.

One of the key developments facing leaders today is information overload, allied with an over-reliance on data. Here's how it works. We have more data at our disposal than ever before. CEOs are well used to data: management reports are the bread-and-butter of business decision-making. They analyse it rigorously and decide what to do: it's what the market expects. But often, people confound the data. When Donald Trump won the 2016 US election, not a single mainstream opinion poll had predicted a win. In a changing world, while data offers ever more predictive opportunities, it also offers more opportunities for us

to allow it to take us down the wrong path. But CEOs rely on it because it is clear and quantitative.

Instead, leaders must move to a synthesising mindset, which can connect the dots of multiple issues, signposted by multiple sources, instinctively, to form the relationships between them. They will appreciate the complexities of a situation without being blinded by the specifics. There is a component of instinct or gut feel; something entrepreneurs credit hugely, but which larger organisations tend to breed out in favour of analytics.

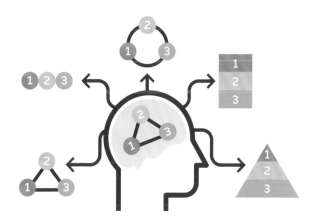

The synthesising mind re-arranges information to help it make sense to itself and others

A simple metaphor would be driving a car. The driverless cars currently in development solve driving challenges by digital brute force – thousands of pieces of numeric analysis every second – rather like the analytical CEO. Yet people drive cars in a totally different way, synthesising triggers from all around (pedestrians, the traffic up ahead, the speed) and making decisions instinctively and by synthesis. Both get results, but the human brain is wired to spot patterns and trends, to organise concepts to create mosaics and meaning; and in so doing, to form something greater than the sum of its parts. While the driverless car is impressive in reading its surroundings and reacting accordingly, it is not yet able to make the nuanced decisions that people can.

The synthesising CEO needs to aspire to the same level of instinct and synthesis. Transcending reactive approaches and, with the confidence of multiple rich sources, a CEO will build a world-view from which she can be better prepared for the future.

She will spot trends and infer meaningful relationships which put her on the cusp of a trend in a way that raw analytics cannot achieve.

HUMAN DOING TO HUMAN BEING

How an evolving appreciation of the self offers leaders untapped resources of resourcefulness to bring to commercial and political challenges

Human Doing to Human Being

VUCA originally comes from the US military in the 1990s. It is an acronym describing the Volatility, Uncertainty, Complexity and Ambiguity in the world as it appeared to be evolving.

An example of **volatility** is how oil prices reached nearly US $155 in 2008, only to drop as low as US $48 later in the year. This didn't just affect Exxon and BP, but everything and everyone from car manufacturers to airlines – imagine how quick they were to rewrite their hedging contracts.

To see **complexity**, take a look at how our global banking system functions. HSBC, NatWest and plenty of others are struggling as (along with other issues) consumer behaviour outpaces layers of IT infrastructure dating back to the 1970s. New high-tech 'challenger banks' are stealing a march on their legacy competitors with agile and, therefore, cheaper service offerings.

In 'Supply Chains to Supply Networks', we explored how HP suffered as a result of the Tōhoku earthquake, which damaged a critical element of its supply chain. That created **uncertainty** as cash flows were threatened – a sentiment amplified in the markets.

Any Western company looking to do business with China will be tempted by a burgeoning middle class and its desire for Western goods. On the flip side, there's risk in parting with intellectual property and a bureaucracy which is perceived as unfathomable to Western eyes. That's **ambiguity**.

Put all these ingredients together, and the challenges facing business leaders have never been greater.

The major challenges of the VUCA world have surprisingly human consequences: they require leaders to be the best version of themselves possible. As explored in 'Analysing to Synthesising,' simple brute force analysis of circumstances won't work in the future – there are too many unknowns. We need something more fundamental. A key element of 'Leadership to Followership' describes how leaders of the future will need to instil confidence in teams and bring followers to the top table. By unlocking the potential of their own resourcefulness, this ability will come naturally – sometimes in ways which are already clear to leadership theorists today and others which are currently unknown; new abilities to ride the wave of uncertainty.

Leaders of the future will come to realise that their own 'operating systems' are what will require fresh understanding. If they do, they will achieve a better 'Quality of Mind,' enabling resourcefulness on a scale never seen before. Quality of Mind is an individual's in-the-moment level of access to the potential of their resourcefulness (known and unknown). It sits at a more fundamental level than skills, knowledge and personality – the traditional measures of leadership.

Video: 'Piers Thurston on Quality of Mind'.
See futuristmatt.com/fonvideos
Hybrid book users: Video 7

Special thanks to Piers Thurston for his invaluable input in creating this section.
See www.makingchangework.co.uk

To some, this will read as somewhat abstract. Let's bring just one element to life. Have you ever experienced a moment when you were so focused on something, you lost all perception of time? It could have been in a moment of danger, while writing, listening to music, or even doing something mundane (I often feel this way when stapling papers and stuffing envelopes). This is known as 'flow state' and is a 'peak state of consciousness where we both feel our best and perform our best. It's available to anyone, anywhere, provided certain initial conditions are met.'

LOW QUALITY OF MIND		HIGH QUALITY OF MIND
Reactive & driven by insecurity	Proactive defaulting to risk averse	Open, curious and vulnerable
Contributions are personally invested, & inconsequential for the group value. Often confusing	Contributions are tangential often to prove a point or demonstrate self worth/value. Often verbose	Contributions solely add relevance for the group seeking clarity and connection. Succinct and insightful
Focuses on difference and separation between people	Confuses and links difference of opinion, with lack of connection	Knows connection is possible with anyone (and often crucial)
Personally invested and blinkered	Balances personal organisational purpose	Sees beyond personal constructs
Feels the need to manipulate and protect from opinions of others	Feels need to influence and reframe others	Trusts the collective wisdom of collaboration and co-creation
Blinkered by insecurity & stuck by past experiences as the reference	Creates from known & fit with their scope of experience	Willing to create from unknown – Sees possibility as growth
Unaware of the impact of their state of mind on communication	Focuses on saying the right things in the right way	Knows the content and style of communication is less important than the 'space' you come from

Some behavioural illustrations of different levels of Quality of Mind

Most of us recognise that we can access an intelligence, clarity, connection and resourcefulness on occasions, which appears to surprise us. Once this ability is harnessed, we know that we can have fresh new perspectives at any moment. This can be leveraged as a true business benefit. What's blocking us is a misunderstanding of the determinants of our Quality of Mind. Leaders of the future will develop alignment with the principles of the human mind. In the same way that years ago society stopped performing animal sacrifices in order to get more rain, we'll stop looking to events and circumstances or our psychology to find answers to modern seemingly intractable problems.

This new understanding will unlock resourcefulness and well-being — it goes beyond positive thinking, mindfulness practices and understanding ourselves in terms of personality and conditioning. It points to reversing a misunderstanding that we have innocently and invisibly been caught up in. For example, contemporary negatives of leadership include stress and anxiety. 'Enlightened' future leaders will recognise these as manifestations of our thoughts, rather than as conditions in themselves, so essentially eradicating them as we might learn to see a mirage in the desert for what it is – simply a figment of our imagination.

To see High Quality of Mind (HQM) traits in a contemporary leader, we only need to look at former President Obama. He listens, connects, is calm and appears to see situations without insecure thinking. Trump represents a contrast. We can also learn from history. Just look towards Mandela or Gandhi, both of whom realised that change needs to come from the inside out. Both exhibited HQM.

Those who were alive in the mid 1990's will remember the trend for 'Magic Eye' images. They are a great metaphor for the invisible nature of quality of mind. At first you can't see the hidden image, then you can. Once you do, the image looks different forever. In a more literal sense, the Magic Eye demonstrates how the brain doesn't process what's in front of it, but sees it as an inside-out projection.

David Eagleman: futuristmatt.com/fonlinks

There's plenty of evidence that pursuing activities like meditation, yoga, clean living, massage, etc. all contribute to a higher Quality of Mind. The revolution we need to realise is that these activities are correlation rather than causation. Work being done by scientists like Dr David Eagleman shows that neuroscience is beginning to point at what spiritualists and mystics have always known. Put simply that humans have the capacity to tap into a vast resourcefulness and well-being at any moment regardless of external circumstances and without performing any aforementioned rituals. That doesn't mean abstaining from these activities, but we just need a better understanding of how the system works, and what causes what.

'WE BELIEVE WE'RE SEEING THE WORLD JUST FINE UNTIL IT'S CALLED TO OUR ATTENTION THAT WE'RE NOT.'

'ARE YOU CONSCIOUSLY TELLING YOUR BRAIN TO JUMP FROM WORD TO WORD IN THIS SENTENCE? OF COURSE, YOU AREN'T, AND THAT'S THE BEAUTY OF THE UNCONSCIOUS BRAIN IN ACTION.'

'THERE IS A LOOMING CHASM BETWEEN WHAT YOUR BRAIN KNOWS AND WHAT YOUR MIND IS CAPABLE OF ACCESSING.'

'IT TURNS OUT YOUR CONSCIOUS MIND – THE PART YOU THINK OF AS YOU – IS REALLY THE SMALLEST PART OF WHAT'S HAPPENING IN YOUR BRAIN, AND USUALLY THE LAST ONE IN LINE TO FIND OUT ANY INFORMATION.'

Dr David Eagleman
Credit: Lawbuffy / Wikimedia Commons

Until we begin to recognise that thought is the source of our experience (as opposed to genetics, environment, personal history or any other external circumstance), we have no choice but to focus our attention on changing those external factors to enhance and improve our experiences and abilities; nor do we need to pump up or understand the self more. Current understanding of the self is a well-heeled illusion that can be seen through. Once it is, leaders will release the full spiritual capacity of being a human being.

The answer lies in understanding how human beings are already designed perfectly to be resourceful, resilient, creative and connected.

THE FUTURE OF WORK

In the 'Leadership' section, we explored some of the characteristics and traits that leaders will need to be successful in the future. Regardless of whether we lead teams, work in organisations or plough our own furrow, we will need to take far more responsibility for our own outcomes in the world of work.

In 'Employee to Free Agent,' we see how more people than ever are opting for (or possibly forced into) free-lance work. A key driver is the growth of 'gig economy' platforms – online labour marketplaces where predo-minantly digitally delivered tasks are bought and sold. This is quite different from the traditional outsourcing model as buyers offer tasks on an as-needed basis while sellers choose when and where they want to work. It creates huge opportunities for progressive organisations that might need periodic skilled capa-city, but wish to avoid additional headcount. We also explore the growing trend of algorithmic manage-ment, in which people work independently, instructed and measured by smartphone apps. This approach is certainly not without its problems.

In 'Future Skills in an Era of New Technology,' we look at the implications for us, the humans, as the techno-logy continues to become more sophisticated. Rese-arch from the World Economic Forum tells us to focus on the skills that machines will find hard to master – a fact that you will hopefully find quite reassuring. For a while yet, AI and robotics will mostly augment rather than replace a lot of jobs.

In 'Professional to Professionalism,' we look at how workers of the future will need to take greater re-sponsibility to nurture their employability and career development. A highly liquid labour pool only serves to increase competition.

The future of work isn't black and white, but it is an engaging topic.

EMPLOYEE TO FREE AGENT

How the gig economy is creating a global and liquid marketplace for human talent – a fine line between opportunity and near-slavery

The Empty Raincoat: futuristmatt.com/fonlinks

Employee to Free Agent

The future of work is a multi-faceted subject and one that's ripe for multiple books, not just a chapter. I'd like to tackle the topic here from a couple of angles. First, the ways in which people are working. Second, the ways in which automation and robotics will augment and sometimes replace people altogether. The way in which people are working has changed dramatically in recent years, with the advent of portfolio careers, a rise in freelancing, the dawning of the 'gig economy' and a move towards algorithmic management. Let's explore each of these in turn.

People with portfolio careers either have several concurrent part-time jobs or a series of jobs, each for a short and overlapping time. To some extent, this can be attributed to reduced job security, but it's also an active choice made by people looking to live more diverse work lives. However, there's a difference between people who have three jobs just to get by and people who have a portfolio of jobs as a career choice. According to Charlie Ball at the careers website, Prospects, 'In 2013, only 20% of those with portfolio careers were doing so because they needed to take more than one job to make a living.' Portfolio careers aren't a new idea. They were popularised by the 1990s management guru, Charles Handy, in his book The Empty Raincoat. The concept was simple – going portfolio was exchanging job security for independence – being our own boss.

There has been a staggering increase in pure freelancers, contractors and temporary employees in recent years. According to the US Bureau of Labor Statistics, 15.5 million people in the US were self-employed in May 2015 – a jaw-dropping 1 million increase on the previous year. According to some forecasts, over 40% of the US workforce (60 million people) will be independent workers by 2020 – a four-fold increase in five years. The UK's Office for National Statistics predicted in 2015 that 4.63 million or 1 in 7 of the working population were self-employed. In addition, a study conducted by online labour exchange Peopleperhour forecast this number to rise to 1 in 2 by 2020, though it doesn't take much critical thinking to guess why an online labour exchange would reach that conclusion.

By 2020, 2 in 5 US workers will be independent

Mobile and other technologies are creating completely new work ecosystems. Indeed, someone I know makes his entire livelihood by splitting his time as a gardener (via mobile app TaskRabbit) and taxi driver (via Uber). He's also been learning web development via online training provider Lynda.com and gaining paid experience by selling his skills on Upwork.com. This may not suit everyone, but for many, digitally facilitated labour exchanges will be the new norm.

With the introduction of the 'gig economy,' 'gigs' are no longer something that only musicians seek out. Ideally, they were paid opportunities to play music at different venues. They helped musicians build up their reputation and (hopefully – although many musicians today would disagree!) generated some cash in the process. Away from music, the 'gig economy' has come to signify much more. Since 2010, we've seen the growth of online platforms matching those who require tasks to be completed (employers of a sort) with those looking to complete tasks (freelancers). For the most part, these tasks are completed digitally. Typical tasks include book-keeping, programming, video editing and much more.

Two of the biggest players are Upwork and Amazon Mechanical Turk, but there is a wealth of other options and some pure-play platforms for specific skills (e.g. voice overs, cleaning, etc.). As someone who ran a creative agency, I was a regular employer on these platforms. We often used them as a place to expand our capacity, either for specific projects (e.g. graphic design, motion graphics) or more routine work such as cleaning databases.

Despite an incredibly fast-moving market, McKinsey&Company estimate that around 540 million workers globally will have used an online platform to find short-term work by 2025.

In 2013, there was a particularly humorous example of this 'personal outsourcing' being taken to its logical conclusion. An employee who became known as 'Programmer Bob' (working with a critical infrastructure firm) was found to have outsourced his entire job to a firm in China, paying a fifth of his annual salary for the privilege. Prior to his subsequent sacking, he was bestowed a 'best programmer in the building' award for his productivity.

The investigation revealed his typical workday included:

ebay

11:30 a.m.
Take lunch

1:00 p.m.
eBay time

facebook

2:00-ish p.m.
Facebook updates, Linkedin

Linked in

reddit

9:00 a.m.
Arrive and surf Reddit for a couple of hours. Watch cat videos

4:30 p.m.
End-of-day update e-mail to management

5:30 P.m.
Go home

Depending on your perspective, 'Bob' was either a model intrapreneur or was guilty of facilitating access to proprietary systems and threatening the firm's information security.

Forward-thinking organisations are well placed to take advantage of these online labour exchanges. They facilitate increased capacity without the associated headcount costs. That said, the 'Bob' example above highlights the importance of putting in place sensible policies, which take account of the associated business risk when using these services.

Not only is proprietary information at risk, but there may be data protection implications as well. Even if your gig economy assistants sign Non-Disclosure Agreements (NDAs), if they are in another territory, are you really going to navigate a foreign legal system to seek redress if your sensitive company documents end up in public hands?

According to Deloitte's 2016 millennial study, 44% of those surveyed plan to leave employers within two years. Additionally, 56% stated they would refuse to work for employers whose values were not congruent with their own. The competition for skilled graduates and early stage career professionals is intense. Philippe De Ridder, co-founder of Board of Innovation says corporates can innovate like start-ups by creating environments more like start-ups. They work with clients who set up 'intrapreneurship' programmes where individuals get full ownership over projects. In addition to greater decision-making, those employees could be free to hire 'as and when needed.' There's little doubt that some of these people will utilise their new skills in setting up their own ventures at a later date.

A selection of key results from Deloitte's 2016 millennial study

ATTRITION
Will leave current employers within 2 years

REFUSAL
To work for employers because of values

PURPOSE
Is more than just performance

SATISFACTION
Inclusive working culture is critical factor

UberEats: futuristmatt.com/fonlinks

For example, a manufacturer could prototype an IoT concept by co-coordinating circuit and CAD designers, user interface specialists and software programmers through one or several of the online platforms available. Not only would this keep bureaucracy to a minimum, but costs are controllable, and the project can quickly be brought to a halt if it shows signs of failure.

It's not all good, though, especially from the freelancers' perspective. There's no doubt these gig economy platforms will favour one group over another. Those employers seeking the lowest possible price will find their workers where living costs are lowest. When labour becomes commoditised, those in the Philippines or India are far better placed to win work than people in the US or the UK. In addition, we'll probably see a huge emerging cohort with no job stability, financial security or opportunities to progress their careers.

Further change is happening in terms of how this work is distributed. We are currently seeing an intermediate step towards full automation, known as algorithmic management. If you live in a major urban development, chances are you'll have seen a host of takeaway and other delivery services sprouting up. One such service is UberEATS, the subsidiary of taxi giant Uber, which launched in June 2016. They promise 'the food you want, from the London restaurants you love, delivered at Uber speed.' What marks it as a trend to watch is that (like Uber drivers), these delivery workers don't have managers, known colleagues or even a hub from which to work. They are managed exclusively by their mobile apps – ultimately by algorithms.

The early promise was a win-win for everyone. Drivers could work the hours that suited them. Restaurants would not be required to increase headcount to make deliveries. Things ran smoothly for a few months – until the app updated. The pay formula changed and many found themselves out of pocket – and angry. 26th August 2016 saw the first London strike by gig workers who felt cheated.

And Uber's not alone. According to this Financial Times article, this algorithmic management goes much further as illustrated by the example of Deliveroo, a similar delivery business:

> *Deliveroo's algorithm monitors couriers closely and sends them personalised monthly 'service level assessments' on their average 'time to accept orders,' 'travel time to restaurant,' 'travel time to customer,' 'time at customer,' 'late orders' and 'unassigned orders.'*
>
> *The algorithm compares each courier's performance to its own estimate of how fast they should have been. An example from one of self employed courier Bhone Kyaw's assessments: 'Your average time to customer was less than our estimate, which means you are meeting this service-level criterion. Your average difference was -3.1 minutes.'*
>
> *Deliveroo confirmed it performs the assessments but said its 'time-related requirements' took into account reasonable delays and riders were 'never against the clock for an order.'*

Algorithmic management is set to grow. Forward thinking organisations would do well to welcome and implement feedback from workers to maintain good relations and avoid disruption to the service.

In summary, portfolio careers will become ever more prevalent, and there's little doubt that the growth of those with freelancer status and increased access to online labour exchanges will revolutionise the future of work. As tasks become increasingly commoditised, those in developed countries will struggle to win work and will be forced to differentiate their offerings to do well. Algorithmic management is also here to stay and arguably represents inevitable steps towards full automation of many jobs. In short, if a job can be automated, it will be.

However, it's not all bleak for workers of the future. In the next section, we'll explore how the things that make us human will be the characteristics that help us thrive in the new age.

FUTURE SKILLS IN AN ERA OF NEW TECHNOLOGY

How we can thrive in an economy in which ever more functions are automated; and the skills we should nurture to do so

Future Skills in an Era of New Technology

Much is written about the demise of jobs due to the rise of machines. Many blue collar jobs were taken by machines during the original industrial revolution, but new ones were created in turn. People learned new skills to create value for society. In the short term, we'll see more automation, but also more augmentation – robots and AI helping us do our jobs better and more safely, rather than replacing us entirely. In many ways the future is bright. It will emphasise the need for us to develop our most human skills and let the machines do what they're best at.

As well as exploring the skills we'll need in the next 10 to 20 years; it's helpful to look at a few jobs that didn't even exist just a decade ago in 2006. We didn't have Social Media Managers as the major platforms – Facebook, Twitter, Instagram – either didn't exist or hadn't broken free of a few college campuses. We didn't have Cloud Computing Specialists. Indeed, the term 'Cloud Computing' is thought to have come from a 2006 conference featuring Google CEO, Eric Schmidt.

And we didn't have YouTube content creators. While the platform existed in 2003, it was only in 2008 that YouTube's Partner Programme went mainstream and allowed users to make money from advertising.

Video: 'Barry Flack on Future Skills and Ways of Working.'
See futuristmatt.com/fonvideos
Hybrid book users: Video 8

Future of Jobs Report 2016: futuristmatt.com/fonlinks

Technology is changing the workplace fast. According to 'The Future of Jobs,' a report by the World Economic Forum, we'll see an interesting shift in desirable skills even by 2020:

Top 10 Skills

WORLD ECONOMIC FORUM

COMMITTED TO IMPROVING THE STATE OF THE WORLD

in 2020	in 2015
1. Complex Problem Solving	1. Complex Problem Solving
2. Critical Thinking	2. Coordinating with Others
3. Creativity	3. People Management
4. People Management	4. Critical Thinking
5. Coordinating with Others	5. Negotiation
6. Emotional Intelligence	6. Quality Control
7. Judgment and Decision Making	7. Service Orientation
8. Service Orientation	8. Judgment and Decision Making
9. Negotiation	9. Active Listening
10. Cognitive Flexibility	10. Creativity

Source: Future of Jobs Report, World Economic Forum

Around a third of those skills don't feature in 2015, and the jump in creativity from 10th to 3rd place in 2020 is notable. In a broad sense, this is in line with the trend of 'what can be automated, will be automated.'

Later, we'll explore some of the areas where AI is making inroads on white collar jobs. Overall, we see a rise in skills that can't easily (and maybe never can) be automated. Emotional intelligence, creativity and critical thinking are all skills that require processes that machines find challenging.

Will our human work become increasingly virtualised? The same report also highlights those job areas on the rise and those decreasing in the lead up to 2020:

Job families in decline and on the rise

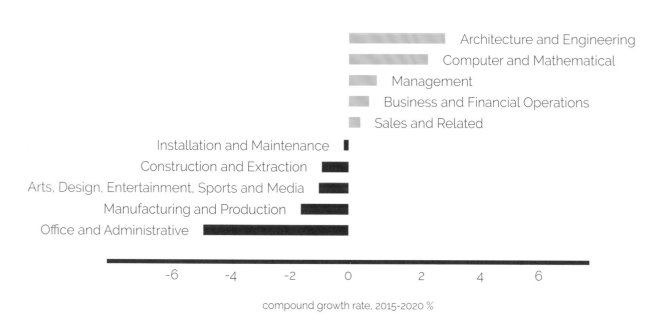

compound growth rate, 2015-2020 %

Source: Future of Jobs Report, World Economic Forum

Which jobs are set to automate?

There's a huge debate going on about what the implications are of massively increased automation. I'm convinced we'll see automation of white collar jobs in the same way blue collar jobs were subsumed during the industrial revolution. Where I'm less convinced, however, is that machines can take on truly human qualities. Take empathy for example. There's just not enough reference information on which to build machine learning.

Sure – I'll put out my status updates and photos on Facebook. But the underlying emotions are slightly more difficult to convey. Indeed, words are too clumsy anyway. Even if a direct neural connection could be made to a machine, would they be capable of true human understanding?

LAWYERS (http://www.rossintelligence.com)

Back in May 2016, we saw the first hire of an AI lawyer in the form of ROSS. The system is built on the back of IBM Watson. 'ROSS' has joined the bankruptcy practice of Baker and Hostetler and works alongside 50 other lawyers. Where systems like ROSS can excel is searching for precedents and answering questions.

HR PROFESSIONALS (https://flatpi.com)

Get ready for platforms like FlatPi to be the ultimate recruiter. It sifts and ranks candidates in seconds rather than days or weeks. No doubt existing HR professionals will argue a case for intuition, but we should expect AI to be taking a greater role in future search and selection.

MARKETING (https://persado.com)

Look out for Persado. It not only generates copy and personalised messaging for clients, but it also automates the online component of your marketing mix too. Oh – and it's been taught all about techniques to persuade, so it's certainly not dumb either!

THERAPIST (http://bit.ly/simsensei)

You'd think that therapy would be the last of the jobs to be automated, but stand corrected. Ellie reads body language through her Kinect sensor and is trained to respond like a human – smiling, nodding, etc. via her screen. I ought to point out Ellie does not make recommendations. Right now – her strengths lie in augmenting human therapists, giving them more real-time insight than they otherwise would.

That said – you might find Ellie in an app store sometime soon.

Ellie reading the micro expressions of her patient.
Credit: The University of Southern California Institute for Creative Technologies

PROFESSIONAL TO PROFESSIONALISM

How the speed of change demands that, whatever our skills or seniority, we must all take more personal responsibility for our career direction

Professional to Professionalism

We are already comfortable with some of the changes we have witnessed in the workplace. We have seen the demise of the idea of a job for life, indeed in many sectors, the average tenure is barely a year. We have also seen the emergence of the 'gig economy,' in which labour is traded globally in open markets on platforms like Upwork and Peopleperhour. Beyond commoditised labour, many people choose the option of a 'portfolio career,' sustaining several roles often using different professional skills and bringing them to many organisations at any one time.

What unites all these work patterns is the idea that a typical career will no longer be linear. On the one hand, organisations can tap into talent as and when they need it in a highly liquid labour pool; on the other, smart people can leverage workplace flexibility to build a lifestyle which is intellectually challenging and in which work fits around other aspects of their lives.

But to achieve this, individuals must nurture their own employability and take responsibility for their own career development. In particular, beyond the sector-specific training which has always been part of the fabric of education (engineering, law, health and safety, etc.), a range of softer and universal skills are becoming highly valued. Technical competence is now just a minimal requirement. Employers – in the now loose sense of 'anyone with money to buy your services' – want to see honesty, integrity, accountability, commitment and emotional intelligence. They want people who will fit, go the extra mile, get on with colleagues, learn new skills and engage across age and departmental boundaries. And of course, in a fluid workplace, businesses want the security of working with people who are 'results-oriented,' i.e. will demonstrably do what they commit to doing. Again, reiterating the importance of 'human skills' as outlined in the previous section.

None of these are technical skills; they are the hallmarks of professionalism, which can be applied to any sector or workplace. And individuals must make it their own business to hone these skills as their careers progress. Smart people recognise both the power and the fragility of their personal offer and are dedicated to improving their skills and maintaining their relevance. They realise that change is the norm, and will constantly find ways to add value in an increasingly complex and unpredictable world. They will achieve this partly the 'official' way, by staying on-point with their skills through training, but also partly by honing an open attitude to working with other people who have other skills; thereby growing emotionally and also living a more fulfilling work-life.

Forward-thinking companies and individuals should be prepared to look outside of their immediate spheres of interest. Google accomplishes this through its 'Talks' series, where sponsored external speakers are invited to offices around the world to present on a diverse range of topics. It's impossible to quantify the new thinking this must have generated both inside and externally to the organisation through the post-event videos. Individuals looking to grow their marketability will do well for themselves by attending good quality industry events, subscribing to relevant newsletters and/or following cutting-edge thinkers in their fields. Any or all of these activities will maintain currency in a fast-moving professional landscape.

Any or all of these activities will maintain currency in a fast-moving professional landscape.

Maggie Stilwell on Why EY (Ernst and Young) removed degree qualification from entry criteria to the firm.

See futuristmatt.com/fonvideos
Hybrid book users: Video 9

🌐 SOCIETY

In 'Stress to Loneliness', we assess how modern life can lead to a sense of isolation that in some cases can be deadly. As we work longer hours, many people are seeking connection via social networks, which are merely simulations of human interaction. As VR and AI technologies grow, the need for mindfulness to avoid more lonely lives will grow too. Opportunities abound to forge new relationships, but humanity must be careful not to commoditise them

In 'Borderless World', we explore how technology opens up more possibilities than ever with new forms of communication, currency and automated translation services. That said, the recent rise of populism in Europe and America could temper things quite significantly indeed.

In 'Ownership to Access,' we show how the idea of subscription digital services is steadily moving into the physical world. On the surface, access to products and services rather than ownership is a good thing – increasing the utility of assets and limiting pay models to when resources are required. We should still be mindful, though, of how the access economy keeps wealth in the hands of owners and that it has the potential to widen social inequality.

In 'Servicing to Activating', we look at how passive forms of service are giving way to active ways of facilitating people to serve themselves. We explore how new technologies are set to impact health and banking, in major part because of the growth of AI and Natural Language Generation. Online services have led customers to become more demanding than ever, seeking immediate satisfaction from companies, 24 hours a day, in what has come to be called 'omnichannel fulfilment.' Equally, businesses know that digital self-service is far cheaper than maintaining stores; which is leading to a digital divide in which less able customers are left deeply unserved.

And finally, in 'The Future of Food,' we explore the natural resource challenges facing us, especially given that the world's population is set to rise by 25% in 2050. That's not just agriculture: think forestry and minerals too, for example. It's not all bad – innovation is well placed to save us, in the form of new forms of food production and land management. Interestingly, there are huge social challenges too. We may have to change our diets to incorporate what are currently less appetising options (locusts for protein, anyone?).

And the developing world is gaining a new appetite for expensive and land-intensive meat, just at the time our planet can least afford it.

STRESS TO LONELINESS

How the 20th Century's malaise, stress, is being replaced by loneliness; and how a more mindful approach may be the solution

World Health Organisation: futuristmatt.com/fonlinks

Stress to Loneliness

Stress is certainly a twenty-first-century ailment, and it manifests itself in many diseases: the World Health Organisation (WHO) predicts that by 2020, half of all diseases will be stress-related. Our mental health, perhaps better described as mental wellbeing, is deteriorating: 1 in 4 UK citizens will experience episodes of mental illness in their lives.

However, stress is only part of the story. It exists in a vicious and co-dependent circle with loneliness. We get stressed because (amongst other causes) we are busy; often busy doing unfulfilling or meaningless activities. That stress means we have less time for the people who matter to us, and this causes loneliness. Loneliness then causes more stress. Even being annoyed by people is positive. The technology we surround ourselves with insulates us from both annoying strangers and even friends. And texting our friends may be informal and quick, but in truth lacks the paralinguistic cues that fulfil our desires for true connection. It's not just our mental wellbeing that benefits from true connection.

A study from Brigham Young University, Utah, concluded that people with a diverse range of good relationships experienced a 50% drop in mortality from heart diseases and cancer. This could, of course, be a case of correlation rather than causation, but it certainly adds up to me.

Bingham Young University: Study on loneliness and mortality: futuristmatt.com/fonlinks

Many aspects of modern life exacerbate the situation. Our devotion to work means that we are more tired. The benefits of mobile working and flexible hours also mean that we spend more time home-working, even in large organisations. Those same organisations often use mobile-working as an opportunity to trim their estates and institute hot-desking, which means employees lose the relationships which are forged by sitting with the same people each day.

Back at home, jump on Facebook and many people have 500 or more friends on their social networks. But not only is this online rather than face-to-face, which therefore lacks intimacy; furthermore, our social networked lives are strictly edited for public consumption. Indeed, social networks give us all the tools we need, groups, pictures, etc. to pick the medium and the audience for any social message. They're often used as broadcast tools, for delaying or removing a face-to-face contact, not tools for enhancing friendships. A study from the University of Miami by Dr Christopher Sanders provides some evidence that over-reliance on social networks has negatively affected face-to-face relationships. Wor-

king with teenagers, he showed that those who used online networks for less than one hour per day had closer and richer relationships with family and friends than those who indicated higher rates of social media usage. Mid-level was considered 1–2 hours and high-level, 2 or more hours.

Incidentally, according to a joint study between the University of Virginia and the University of British Columbia, 1 in 10 students have checked their phones during sex.

University of Virginia/British Colombia: Study on smartphones and student use: futuristmatt.com/fonlinks

These issues will continue to challenge modern society. Virtual reality (VR) and artificial intelligence (AI) technologies will allow us to become ever more disconnected from the people around us if we let them, requiring our mindfulness to ensure more positive human connections. The workplace, meanwhile, is in line for a series of changes which are almost entirely unpredictable. We may be forced to work harder by economic pressures. Equally, technologists predict with alarming regularity that advances in technology will render over 50% of current jobs obsolete by 2025. Perhaps this will mean we will have more time for each other.

The jury's out, but whatever the outcome we need to rediscover the importance of shared human experiences and value them for their contribution to our lives. Even when we do choose to get close–really close–to one another, dating apps like Tinder can make the experience a commodity rather than something more engaging and meaningful. This outsourcing of 'relationships' is being taken to a new level by services like 'tinderdoneforyou.com' which promises to 'skip the endless swiping and messaging, and instantly fast-forward to a calendar that's jam-packed with attractive women looking for a good time with a great guy.' The danger here is that human relationships become ever more transactional, further eroding our empathy for the people around us. Healthy relationships are about being in real touch with other real people–our sometimes foolish, flawed conflictual and challenging selves; not a collection of edited avatars.

Mark Zuckerberg at Mobile World
Congress, February 2016.
Credit: Mark Zuckerberg/Facebook

People are waking up to this fact. Look towards groups like Sunday Assembly who create secular congregations in over 70 locations and 8 countries where 'people sing songs, hear inspiring talks and create community together.' The community-driven model has worked so well that the organisation is being hired to replicate the model for social purpose housing associations.

Video: Liz Slade, Sunday Assembly
The rise of loneliness in society
and what shes doing to combat it

See futuristmatt.com/fonvideos
Hybrid book users: Video 10

We can also expect to see continued growth in specialist digital detox holidays where the watchword is 'wifi-free.'

Images from various Sunday
Assembly congregations
Credit: Liz Slade / Sunday Assembly

77

BORDERLESS WORLD

How globalisation has presented
ordinary people with opportunities
beyond their own environments – but
also created radical social backlash

Westphalian Sovereignty: futuristmatt.com/fonlinks

John Kerry, US Secretary of State, said in his commencement speech to the 2016 Northeastern University graduates:

"The future demands from us something more than a nostalgia for some rose-tinted version of a past that did not really exist in any case. Youre about to graduate into a complex and borderless world. "

The context, unfortunately, was his views on the particular dangers of borderless terrorism. His comments were also a pointed barb against Donald Trump, who presented a more isolationist view of the world and its challenge with his remarks on building a wall between Mexico and the US.

The reality is that we live in an age where borders are more porous. The evidence of this is not incontrovertible: the barriers springing up across southern and eastern Europe (for the first time since the Second World War) in response to the Middle-Eastern refugee crisis suggest that borders are protected like never before. But the Westphalian model is about authority; and people's sense of belonging or the validity of institutions which exert power over them is becoming less meaningful. There are also our virtual borders, which have to all intents and purposes evaporated completely. Technology is enabling the rise of a global citizenry in ways we couldn't comprehend even 10 years ago. While it's difficult to define the 'Global Citizen,' a 2016 poll carried out by the BBC World Service of 20,000 people in 18 countries found that over half considered themselves global rather than national citizens.

Indeed, how many of us live in one place, but work in another, or travel to different places as a matter of routine? How many of us work in virtual teams? Teleconferencing, Skype and other ubiquitous communication tools make collaborating with colleagues

BBC 'Global Citizen' poll: futuristmatt.com/fonlinks

Oculus Rift: futuristmatt.com/fonlinks

WeWork 'Welive' apartments: futuristmatt.com/fonlinks

across the world straightforward, though not always necessarily comfortable. Many companies use Skype video to collaborate with team members globally when working on new products. Very soon, that'll be VR technologies such as Oculus Rift which will enable them to examine new product concepts from every angle, perhaps even involving haptic sensors to enable a sense of look and feel. VR will not only facilitate dispersed office environments but also allow teams to 'go anywhere,' for example to a manufacturing facility to really get a feel for what's happening on the ground.

Companies are beginning to close physical offices completely. Indeed, one US-headquartered software company (that wished to remain anonymous), built a strategy in 2014 to 'consolidate office facilities' and to 'expand work from home.' This lead to a large number of resignations as many staff felt unsettled by the changes. Of course, we've been here before: companies like the US ad agency Chiat Day were at the forefront of hotdesking: saving money on facilities by owning only the resources necessary to house an average number of people at any one time. It has

had its downsides: employees used to their personal Post-It notes and cactus on the desk felt alienated and unsettled. But improvements in technology and the cultural norms of the millennial generation, happy to work with a laptop and nothing else, are making the 'anywhere economy' a reality.

In 2010, the natural incubation environment of a start-up was the local Starbucks. In 2017, start-ups are not only incubated in a coffee shop but built by developers in Ukraine and Venezuela. We're also seeing the growth of communal live/work spaces offering affordable accommodation and working space to younger people. It started with the now defunct Campus based in San Francisco where young professionals could secure a bed and desk for $30 a night while building their start-up businesses. Although Campus died due to the founders not being able to make it commercially viable, others have sprung up. WeWork's new WeLive spaces do a similar thing in New York and continue to grow. No doubt we'll see more in times to come.

As we become decentralised and denationalised, many feel the very essence of our cultural identities is being eradicated, with language possibly becoming the first victim. Established back in 2006, the Google Translate service is now widely used for quick and easy translations. Originally only text-based, it now supports speech, images and real-time video through a range of interfaces, particularly our smartphones. Google, Microsoft (Cortana) and Apple (Siri) are betting big on spoken interfaces, and it's entirely natural that they should seek to eliminate the complexity of foreign languages, too – especially as they also have billions of reference sentences provided by consumers to build algorithms around.

Skype's Translator service, for example, will take a creditable stab at voice and video calls in seven languages and instant message texts in 50! Real-time translation will soon melt away language as a barrier. The Universal Translator, as seen in Star Trek, is a little more challenging because translation needs context. Say 'Kick the bucket' to an English person, and they'll know that you mean 'to die'. Translate that into Mandarin, and a Chinese person will take it literally –

with presumably amusing consequences. But that's not stopping a raft of companies from having a go. The Waverly Labs pilot – which bears a remarkable resemblance to the Babelfish of The Hitch Hiker's Guide to the Galaxy fame – is kicking up a stir on the Indiegogo crowdfunding platform, and is set to ship in 2017.

Video: The Pilot Translator, Waverley Labs – Is near simultaneous language translation becoming a reality?

See futuristmatt.com/fonvideos
Hybrid book users: Video 11

Plenty more issues stand in the way – for example handling accents – but the three motivations of innovation for innovation's sake, our desire to use speech now that smartphones are our default devices, and the infinite marketing/monetisation possibilities of linguistic parity make language a fertile ground for breaking down the borders between humans wherever they may be. As machine translation sophistication grows, it's entirely possible that niche companies will emerge specialising in complex documents such as those found in the legal and financial arena.

That said, it can be tiresome for businesses making occasional cross-border payments. In particular, traditional banks have rested on their laurels for far too long, extracting profit from the ignorance of the ordinary and ill-informed consumer. Transferwise, one of the few British 'Unicorns' (businesses valued at over $1 billion) is a good answer to this problem, facilitating simple peer-to-peer money transfer. It benefits users by not actually 'exchanging' money, but simply matching users from one country to another and paying out from a local account. Because money doesn't

TransferWise

There's no doubt it's getting easier for people to transact. For the average consumer, online payments have never been more straightforward. Apple Pay (and Android Pay which is rolling out currently) have pushed contactless spending above £1.5 billion per month for the first time, according to the UK Cards Association.

actually 'move,' no banking transfer fees apply. Added to which, individuals and SMEs get access to actual mid-market rates, simply paying a fixed fee for the transaction.

On top of the challenge of a lack of expertise, currency devaluations can add to problems. In Russia in 2014, for example, crashing oil prices and political instability saw the ruble tumble. Intriguingly, the reaction of many people – especially the country's enormously tech-savvy youth – was to invest (or protect value) in Bitcoin. Bitcoin is the poster child for so-called 'Cryptocurrencies' – currencies that are not tied to a specific sovereignty.

They do away with hefty transaction fees and render obsolete the rules and regulations around transfers. There are huge risks with Bitcoin – if nothing else, the liquidity of the Bitcoin marketplace is completely unproven. But even if Bitcoin is a trailblazer which ultimately fails, the identity and transaction authority technology which underpins it, Blockchain, has attracted the interest and investment of many banks, including Barclays, BBVA, Credit Suisse, JP Morgan, State Street, Royal Bank of Scotland and UBS.

These are just a few examples of the new globalisation, giving individuals access to a world without borders. We can speak, make money and market ourselves without considering location, national loyalty or any other traditional constraint. However, this should all be tempered by an apparent rise of so called populism across the world. Brexit and the ascendancy of President Trump are setting a trend that individual countries should do what's purely in the interest of their own sovereignty.

If the trend continues to grow around the world, we may start to see borders suddenly become more meaningful than ever.

OWNERSHIP TO ACCESS

How finite resources and the mindset of the millennial generation are devaluing ownership and building an economy of rental, subscription and usage

The definition of wealth is changing. We will own fewer physical goods, but have access to more overall, thanks to simple online marketplaces which handle the complexities of resource management and availability to give us the things we need on-demand.

Want a car? Try Zipcar – where you pay by the hour or buy a monthly or yearly subscription which includes a predefined mileage each month.

Need a dress for that special night out? My Secret Dressing Room is there to help with outfits, bags and shoes for the night. And users of these services get simple, by-the-hour rental without any of the hassles of ownership. There's no need to maintain, back up, clean or store things, and you only pay for what you use. In many cases, as with My Secret Dressing Room's luxury clothing, this gives users access to products which would otherwise not be financially viable.

Credit: Zipcar.co.uk

My Secret Dressing Room: futuristmatt.com/fonlinks

Microsoft Azure: futuristmatt.com/fonlinks

Amazon Web Services: futuristmatt.com/fonlinks

The access economy works for everyone. Not only users of these services are happy but also the owners of assets – it can be a way to monetise them when they are not in use. Most cars, for example, are only in use 3% of the time – to be able to profit from this downtime is a win-win, especially as cars have a high fixed cost of ownership in terms of maintenance and taxation. As there is a general shift to more crowded cities, where storage space is at a premium, it makes more sense for us, and for the environment, to own less, consume less, and share more.

This trend is being seen in business, too. Office space is shared on short leases and resource managed through hot-desking. Unused media slots on TV and radio can be sold on or subbed out. The entire principle of Cloud digital services exploits the economies of scale that come with many users sharing the same computers, security protection and backups; and then also benefiting from the total agility of being able to scale up or down on demand. Amazon Web Services and Microsoft Azure can both provision massive web services in minutes – the sort of systems which would previously have required 6 months and mil-lions of pounds in expenditure. The access economy breeds flexibility, allowing entrepreneurs to build more nimble businesses, which are either more pro-fitable or can exploit their leanness to find viability in new niches. The ability to facilitate its users scaling ambitions is one major reason why Amazon Web Services turnover doubled from $428 million in Q3 2015 to $861 million in Q3 2016.

The sharing economy creates two types of company. Zipcar owns its fleet of cars and makes its money by minimising costs and maintaining a high usage rate. Other ventures oil the wheels of the sharing economy by acting solely as a marketplace – Streetbank, for example, is a local sharing service for building tools. Most drills are only used five times, yet someone within 400 metres of your home probably has one they could lend you.

I don't need a drill.
I need a hole in the wall

Streetbank: futuristmatt.com/fonlinks

There are some caveats. Sharing services have become particularly popular as the recession bites. There are warnings that they pander to a deeper propagation of social inequality: low-end wages are stagnating, and the sharing economy keeps wealth in the hands of property owners. And only owners can modify, customise and control the use of property. Only owners can give away or bequeath property. That said, the ability to improve and personalise shared assets in the access economy no doubt represents an opportunity for the new breed of entrepreneurs coming through.

The ownership to access trend is set to grow, with PwC estimating the global access economy will increase from £9 billion in 2014 to £230 billion in 2025.

SERVICING TO ACTIVATING

How technology like AI is allowing consumers more control on their terms, creating demand for immediacy and responsiveness from business

We're entering a world of easy self-service. Many of you will use online banking, whether through a website, smartphone or even chatbot via your messenger app of choice. Many of us no longer need to visit banks to ask for customer service. We simply fire up an app to make transfers, check balances, apply for loans and so on. That's 'Activating.' In this section, we look at the effect of activating on two sectors: health and business.

Changing health behaviours is hard. It's not a logical process. For example, 1 in 16 people in the UK have diabetes; this is expected to increase to around 1 in 10 by 2025. Yet many diabetics struggle to make long-term, sustained changes to their lifestyles, even though they are on constant medication and know that the prognosis is anything from a shortened life to painful amputation. We are not good at following advice – especially when that advice comes from visits to the doctor which may be months apart and involves being constantly mindful of our condition.

One solution enabled by technology is regular and highly personalised prompting from automated systems. This may be as simple as apps which remind us to take complex permutations of pills at the right time, but there is also ample evidence that encouraging behavioural change is an incremental, step-by-step process. For example, we all know that giving up smoking is easier for most people if we cut down first. Especially in healthcare, the need for a nudge is ever more important in the world of choice. We all know that we need to make sustainable choices to stay healthy, but the complexities of a sedentary lifestyle and the high-budget techniques of marketers persuading us to enjoy sugary drinks mean that all too often we make not bad choices but lazy choices. We need a voice of conscience in our pocket to keep us on the right track.

'Can I Eat It?' is a beautifully designed app which allows users to scan a barcode while shopping to immediately see the nutritional value of any food product. A simple 'thumbs up, thumbs down' will show an assessment of the product for salt, fat, sugar and other content. Better still, the data is crowdsourced, so users know that they are part of a community of health change. Then there's Runkeeper, which not

Can I Eat it app: futuristmatt.com/fonlinks

Runkeeper: futuristmatt.com/fonlinks

only offers workouts and challenges starting from the most basic 'learn to run,' but also offers discounts from partner brands to make keeping fit a genuinely rewarding experience. It offers audio cues so that users can be motivated on each circuit – and you'll hear them because you'll be listening on headphones to your personalised Spotify playlist.

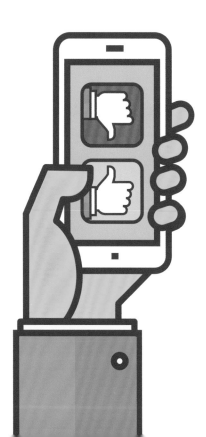

These are only two examples, but they exhibit some of the key factors in making health engagement work. 'Can I Eat It?' makes healthy choices a little more hassle-free – it removes some of the complexity of sticking with the programme. And Runkeeper is richly personalised to make the experience engaging and fun. These lead to the holy grail: self-management and improvement of health issues in a resource-constrained care system. Indeed, Britain's National Health Service (NHS) plans to give away millions of devices and apps in April 2017 to help reduce patient deaths and enable better management of diseases such as diabetes and heart disease. No doubt, it's a cost cutting exercise too, but it also points towards how citizens will be expected to self-serve their own healthcare needs more in the future.

As outlined in the introduction, banking is already an industry well versed in self-service. A technology on the cusp of transforming activation is chatbots. These are software programs integrated into messaging applications such as Facebook Messenger, WhatsApp, Viber and WeChat. Unlike traditional app interfaces which tend to be more button and form based, chatbots communicate via text and voice commands, in an increasingly conversational language style.

As part of a talk I gave at the end of 2016, I presented a fictional example of how a chatbot could be used for banking.

In the image, we see a customer instigate the saving of money. It's a smooth experience, easily understood by the customer and transacted quickly by the chatbot which is able to interact with underlying banking systems.

Underpinning Chatbot technology are three key factors. First is the growth of machine understanding – the ability to make sense of user requests. Second is natural language generation – the ability to communicate meaningfully with the user. And third is the seamless integration with the underlying service. The banking example highlights the way in which the customer requests the transfer and how the chatbot then enacts it.

Users will no longer need to download a special app, but can instead interact with a variety of brands from their messenger programme of choice. It will facilitate users getting things done quickly, especially given that their messenger app will know important details including their address, payment information, details of contacts and more. There are still a few details to get right first. One – the user experience has to be extremely smooth, with no mistakes. Two – if users are conducting multiple brand interactions via a messenger app, security needs to be tight!

The opportunities for activation are abundant. Brands can develop smoother onboarding, service and retention processes. But also, internal, low-level processes will become automated. Managing travel, filtering emails, setting to-do reminders and conducting research are all prime uses for the technology. Expect to see more chatbots offering help with ordering products and services, informing customers of delays and, no doubt, a new breed of concierge services will emerge.

As of December 2016, we saw Google Home and Amazon Echo enter top seller charts for Christmas gifts. These are both voice activated 'helpers.' They embody the chatbot principle by answering questions, adjusting the home environment, telling you the news and more. The Amazon Echo even lets customers reorder products.

Provided security and user experience is addressed properly, the future for chatbots is a bright one!

Are you sure you want to reorder 32 inch waist jeans?

THE FUTURE OF FOOD

How advances in food production and land management are tackling the major challenges of population growth

The UN predicts global population is set to rise by 2.5 billion by 2050. Effectively, that's adding a population the size of China and India combined. It will require us to double our food production output. Throw in the fact that 1 in 9 current inhabitants of our planet is 'chronically hungry' right now, and we've a significant challenge on our hands.

A number of factors influence this food crisis. Lifestyles, income and social organisation determine consumption levels. Technology and its availability and application heavily influence whether farming is sustainable or damages the environment, along with the corresponding levels of waste once acquired by people. Inequality is a third factor: land distribution is increasingly held by smaller groups of wealthier landholders.

But the fundamental growth in population really acts as a multiplier to all these. Per capita availability of grains (which make up 80% of the world's food) has declined over the past 25 years. Furthermore, despite being critically polluted or over-farmed in some parts, our oceans are under-utilised: 99% of global food supply comes from land, with less than 1% from oceans or other aquatic farming.

Overuse of farmland, deforestation and indiscriminate use of agri-chemicals also negatively affect water resources, which cycles through to a continued reduction in land quality. Indeed, over a third of the world's agricultural land has been abandoned in the past 40 years because of erosion or deterioration in quality. Sometimes, water is simply not available where it used to be, which matters because agricul-

10 bn.

Population

7.4 bn.

2017   Year   2050

ture consumes around 87% of the world's fresh water. The environmental cost is exacerbated by fossil fuels, essential for the production of pesticides, fertilisers and to power the machines which are replacing human labour. Around 80% of the world's fossil fuels are used by developed and mechanised countries; most of the rest is used in developing countries which need to find markets to compete in.

Human factors such as market forces are also a challenge, for example, the problem of ineffective food distribution. The Grocery Manufacturers Association (GMA) states that 'In the US alone, 215 meals per person go to waste annually.'

Demand for organic food is climbing fast in wealthier countries. People are better informed about food than ever, and many are gravitating towards food that minimises synthetic fertilisers, chemical pesticides, hormones and antibiotic animal treatments. According to US Department of Agriculture estimates, organic food sales in 2005 were valued at around US $13 billion. By 2014 it had almost tripled to approximately US $35 billion. Factoring in wider markets including developing

countries, demand for organic food is expected to rise 16% from 2015 to 2020 according to a report by Techsci.

You might think that the challenge for organic is productivity. As our population grows, so does demand for food. Organic agriculture just doesn't yield the same quantities of food for the land used. Looking at cereals such as corn and wheat, or vegetables, the trend is clear – organic production methods deliver 25% less yield than non-organic.

Current food production is more than enough for every man, woman and child on the planet (organically produced or not). Our real challenge, then, is distribution and waste, accounting for 1.3 billion tonnes (nearly a third), whether that's at the point of harvest, storage or after usage.

1/3 of Global Food production is wasted each year

Food traceability from farm to fork matters even more as supply chains increase in complexity. Food scandals are on the rise. In June 2015, Chinese authorities seized over 100,000 tonnes of frozen meat – some of it up to 40 years old! Whilst, not a health risk as such, we shouldn't forget the 2013 'horsemeat' scandal in which traces of horsemeat DNA were found in UK beefburgers. What it signified was the importance of traceability in food production to prevent serious and systemic harms.

Modern food supply chains consist of multiple layers, which are often opaque yet highly dynamic, affected by currency fluctuations, climatic conditions and consumer sentiment to name but a few influencing factors. These ingredients make it tough to give a fully verified view across the entire chain. Even organic supply chains are hard to verify – they are subject to the same complexities through processing to finished goods as anyone else.

From the consumer standpoint, we are reliant on accurate food labelling that is also comprehensively explained to us. Things are slowly getting better. On 20th May 2016, the US Food and Drug Administration announced enhanced nutrition facts labels for packaged foods. Labels will now include information about diet and chronic disease, helping buyers to make better-informed choices about what they purchase and eat. Additionally, From 13 December 2016, the EU enforced significantly increased nutritional labelling regulations on pre-packed food products. These include everything from declarations of allergens through to marking drinks with a high caffeine content as unsuitable for children and pregnant women.

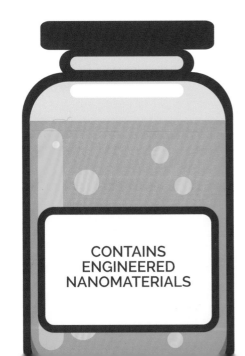

CONTAINS
ENGINEERED
NANOMATERIALS

We have looked at the challenges facing food production today, and now we'll explore how innovation is set to overcome many of the problems detailed here. Let's begin with our overloaded landmass. We have seen how 99% of global food production comes from cultivated land and only 1% from oceans and the aquatic environment. What if we didn't have to give up our land for non-food related products such as ethanol (biofuel), but instead could harness our oldest source of value: the sea?

Companies like Cellena are doing just that with their work in commercial algae production. Consider that commercial algae farms can produce 5,000–10,000 gallons of algae oil per acre compared to just 350 gallons of ethanol per acre when produced by growing crops like maize. Also factor in that algae grows very quickly, even in polluted water or stagnant areas where food crops cannot survive, and society might be onto a winner. Algae is also thoroughly multi-purpose: as well as a fuel, algae can be used as a fertiliser for existing food crops. And it takes CO_2 from the atmosphere – making it nature's ultimate carbon reprocessing as well as freeing up cultivated land for food production.

Cellena: futuristmatt.com/fonlinks

10,000 gallons oil

350 gallons oil

WATER
ALGAE OIL

LAND
ETHANOL

In other innovative advances, we saw the first 'cultured' meat production in 2013, in which a lab-grown beefburger was presented to the world. By all accounts, it didn't taste great, but it did suggest the possibility that meat production doesn't have to be linked to the slaughtering of animals.

Why does cultured meat matter? Well, as Western eating habits spread to China and other fast emerging economies, so does the pressure to open up new farmland. But farming animals is environmentally costly. Cattle occupy around 25% of all cultivatable land, and the crop production to feed them another 25%. If we look at the US, around 70% of grain and cereals grown are fed to farm animals. And 18% of total greenhouse gas emissions stem from the farming of animals.

Livestock farming also consumes alarming amounts of water: it takes between 5,000 and 20,000 litres of water to produce a kilogramme of beef. Companies like Memphis Meat are at the forefront of cultured meat production, especially now that drought is becoming a regular feature of the climate in parts of the US.

Illustration showing the process of creating cultured meat

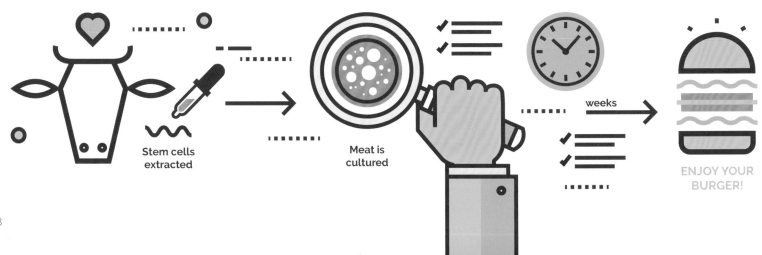

Stem cells extracted

Meat is cultured

weeks

ENJOY YOUR BURGER!

JORDAN

Agriculture in the desert seems unlikely at first, but Charlie Paton, a British inventor, envisions huge seawater greenhouses which could be used both to generate power and grow food. There's nothing complicated about it. He simply proposes using the natural water cycle: seawater is heated by the sun, evaporates, condenses, then returns to the crops as rain.

Consider the recent Sahara Forest Project venture. A greenhouse the size of four football fields has been built in southern Jordan, near the port of Aqaba. If successful, the plan is to create a 20-hectare facility.

But that's relatively small scale. One of the benefits of seawater greenhouses is that they are built on giving nature a helping hand, rather than starting expensively from scratch. That allows some grand visions to develop, like Africa's Great Green Wall. Since 1952, a plan has existed to create a forest 15km wide and 7,775km long, stretching from Senegal to Djibouti. Originally the idea was to contain desertification. What if innovation could facilitate seawater irrigation of a project this size? This goes to show that the potential for food production is immense.

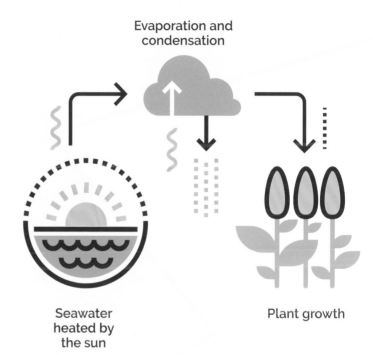

Evaporation and condensation

Seawater heated by the sun

Plant growth

 Aqaba

Crunchy Critters: futuristmatt.com/fonlinks

A further way to increase our food options is to open our minds to new possibilities. Insects are fantastic sources of protein, high in calcium and iron, and low in fat and cholesterol. Farming them doesn't need much space either. At least 1,400 varieties are eaten in Africa, Asia and Latin America already. As goods prices rise and cultivated land becomes more precious, it's perhaps time we saw more insect farms in the Western world. Demand for meat (our current major protein source) is expected to double by 2050 from the turn of the millennium, and we have already seen that meat is incredibly costly to produce. Insects are a plentiful and profitable answer. Businesses are already setting up to cater to this opportunity: go to Crunchy Critters, and you can buy everything from ants to scorpions. Look at the details of their offerings, and you'll see their marketing is still quite playful. 'Ideal for use in Bush Tucker Challenge charity fundraising events' is a bullet point that features about canned tarantulas.

To go mainstream in The West, though, we will need to change our palates – which is a challenge. An alternative is to use insects earlier in the food cycle – you can now buy flour made from Crickets. Garlic cricket bread may sound odd today, but if it doesn't look or taste particularly different from what we are used to, it might just be a perfect solution. Even our institutions are recognising the phenomenon. The EU is offering member states €3m to help promote the use of insects in cooking and has even asked food standards agencies to look at opportunities to supplement diets. The PROteINSECT project believes it may be possible to reduce vegetable and domestic waste by 60% while rearing insects.

EU Insect Grant: futuristmatt.com/fonlinks

Fried Bamboo Insect dinner from Taiwan

Credit: Flying Pterdodacyl / Flickr

Edible Growth: futuristmatt.com/fonlinks

One interesting benefit of 3D printing is how it can convert ingredients in the print process. For example, the 3D heat-and-cool process can be used to extract proteins from algae (our new multi-purpose friend as discussed previously) or insects and then combine them with interesting flavours. Do you remember The Big Bang Theory's Sheldon serving Leonard a 'Mango Caterpillar Snow Cone'? Imagine that, but taken much, much further! Initiatives like Edible Growth are innovating by making seeds, yeast and spores core ingredients.

3d printed pizza for Astronauts!

Systems and Marterials Research Corporation: futuristmatt.com/fonlinks

One of the most advanced 3D food printers has been created by the Systems & Materials Research Corporation (SMRC) – the same people who famously built the machine that printed a pizza for NASA astronauts in 2014.

There are others in the market. Like chocolate? There's even a 3D printer for providing personalisation opportunities for it. See Cocojet's link for more information.

For a healthier example, are you on a low-calorie diet, but still like your burgers? Why not create the bap from insect flour – which will be available and customisable.

As well as unlocking sustainable ingredients, Dutch applied research institute TNO is also using the precision of food printing to improve our health. The business designs meals with precise quantities of nutrients for individual consumers, based on their personal health data and requirements. Additionally they too see the potential of alternative proteins, like algae

Cocojet: futuristmatt.com/fonlinks

TNO: futuristmatt.com/fonlinks

and insects, as components in food. As innovation from organisations like TNO grows, so will the need for their raw materials. This may well kick-start greater investment in algaculture or insect farming.

Those with specific nutritional needs will be able to address them easily. A pregnant woman will get all the Omega 3's she'll need. An athlete will be able to specify the ratios of protein and carbohydrates he consumes to ensure an optimum balance. We could even see reductions in diabetes, heart disease and obesity.

Expect to see previously impossible shapes and textures. If you thought chefs like Heston Blumenthal are at the cutting edge of the scientific approach, don't be surprised to see a completely new type of celebrity emerge as people figure out innovative ways of working with food at the atomic level. I may not want to eat a banana that incorporates the taste of egg, but I like the idea that it's possible!

We're still a way off from the Star Trek replicator, but maybe not as far as we think.

Video: 'Dr Peter Dijken on cutting edge food production and personalisation'

See futuristmatt.com/fonvideos
Hybrid book users: Video 12

 **MEDIA** //73

One of the key themes emerging from the previous section about the future of food is the opportunity for personalisation afforded by 3D printing. That same ability to personalise now extends into the way media is created and consumed.

In 'User-Generated Content,' we look at how content production and distribution has shifted into the hands of customers. In many cases, the personal approach has unleashed previously unknown levels of creativity. However, it's both a blessing and curse to brands whose stock price can rise and fall based on reputation.

In 'Filter Bubbles,' we look at how personalised content feeds run the risk of us believing that our world-views are shared by everyone else. If we are to make sense of the world and make balanced decisions, access to diverse ideas is critical. That's not only made more difficult by algorithms serving us content that they believe we want; in the 'post-truth' world, even audio-visual media can easily be manipulated through consumer-grade tools.

The filter bubble concept entered mainstream conversation at the end of 2016, and we'll examine why this has come to pass.

USER-GENERATED CONTENT

How media titans are being supplanted by a groundswell of creativity and direct engagement which puts global access in everyone's hands

TripAdvisor: futuristmatt.com/fonlinks

VW Dieselgate: futuristmatt.com/fonlinks

User-Generated Content

The concept of user-generated content (UGC) is not new. It first came to the attention of business analysts in the early 2000s, when it became apparent that companies like Facebook were becoming corporate behemoths not by churning out their own content, but by leveraging the value of content created by users. In a sense, Google was the first UGC business: its value is predicated entirely on managing our relationship with billions of other people's internet pages.

For marketers today, however, UGC must be carefully managed. Customers can make or break a brand through reviews and social media. Yelp and TripAdvisor are good examples of collated and ranked UGC. On Twitter and Facebook, brands are entirely at the mercy of popular opinion. Users are no longer passive recipients of brand image. Instead, they are co-contributors to the popular perception of brands, changing brand positions just by the way they talk about them online. And it's not easy for companies to control what others say about them.

For example, the scandal over Volkswagen and emission tests saw a massive backlash from social media users about emissions, spawning the damaging hashtags #dieselgate, #vwgate and #volkswagenscandal. By late September 2015, VW's stock had dropped by 50% of its value. Negative social media and UGC certainly played a major part in the propagation of this PR nightmare.

Yelp: futuristmatt.com/fonlinks

Sandra Macleod, CEO,
www.mindfulreputation.com

In this post-truth, post-trust world, evidence is clear that intangibles such as reputation are fundamental to the financial success of companies. The chill wind blowing through the corporate world in the face of uncontrollable UGC and the shrapnel-like AI-generated 'falsehoods' aiming to harm, damage and challenge, is the latest body-blow to corporate communications. Companies looking to take employees, consumers, investors, and other stakeholders with them through this choppy journey are advised to redouble and strengthen their commitment to transparency, rigorous honesty, clarity and improvement based on shared goals and ambitions. Theirs must be the trusted voice if they are to be heard and survive ahead and only through that hard-nosed dedication and mindful care, will they get there.

Reputation may be intangible but it has a very tangible value. In 2016 alone, corporate reputations contributed £790bn of shareholder value – over a third of the total market capitalisation in the FTSE 350. And that is growing. It is made up of many component parts and consumed variously by those stakeholders that can make or break companies ahead. These things can and should be measured, understood, protected in our increasingly complex and changing world. For those who get it wrong, or focus on short-term numbers alone, the road ahead will be short.

However, not all instances of UGC shaping our perceptions are so clear cut. What about the National Environment Research Council, who opened a Twitter competition to name their new ship? Earlier in 2016, their new research vessel was on the brink of being named Boaty McBoatface. This was either an amusing (and not particularly costly) negative outcome or one of the best pieces of marketing by a dowdy scientific institution in decades. By May 2016, it was named RRS Sir David Attenborough after the well-known naturalist and broadcaster.

It's not all bad news, though. Brands can work with audiences to create incredibly positive coverage, translating into hard profits. One of the most famous UGC campaigns was in 2009, run by Tourism Queen-

Tourism Queensland: futuristmatt.com/fonlinks

sland. Titled 'The best job in the world,' people were invited to submit videos of themselves describing why they should win a 6-month job 'caretaking' a paradise island. The campaign received over 35,000 applications from 200 countries and generated US $70 million of global publicity for an initial investment of US $1 million.

What these examples teach us is that UGC is a tiger which brands have no choice but to grab by the tail. It acts as an amplifier, both for good news and bad. As content production shifts, content co-creation becomes the new norm, and every business is along for the ride, whether they like it or not. UGC is growing inexorably, and it works because users believe it does. Prior to the 2015 General Election, a staggering one-third of 18–24 year olds polled by Ipsos MORI believed their voting decision would be influenced by social media.

There are many challenges surrounding UGC, such as how to filter new UGC information for relevance, reputation and ultimately decision-making – to discern 'the signal from the noise.' Secondly, how to respond reliably and effectively to a user-generated opinion, both positive and negative. Finally, how to react to the ugly truth – the crowd is not always right and has not always thought through its arguments.

The landscape of user-generated content is not immune to change. Facebook and Instagram have both been criticised recently for tweaking their newsfeed displays to either favour advertisers or encourage more participation. Facebook has seen sharing fall, and Twitter usage rates have, according to some analysts, plummeted dramatically.

We can therefore guarantee that social media reputation management for brands is not going to be a colour-by-numbers affair – it demands constant attention.

Ipsos Mori: futuristmatt.com/fonlinks

FILTER BUBBLES

How our world-views are at risk of degradation by the algorithms which attempt to manage our daily information overload

The first giants of the internet made very successful businesses out of putting as much information as possible in front of users, allowing them to make powerfully informed decisions. Look at eBay, which lets us search for millions of items around the globe, rather than being restricted to our local small ads newspaper. We bought flights, read newspapers and found insurance bargains by removing informational disadvantage.

But today, we're stuck in information overload. The technology world's universal solution has been to filter relentlessly. Our media consumption is increasingly designed and personalised to our profiles, often without us even knowing. Google's personalised search and Facebook's personalised news feed are good examples. Your Facebook feed is by no means a simple timeline; instead, algorithms make guesses about what you want to see based on factors such as location, your past click behaviour and search history.

This is especially seductive now that multiple platforms share information and browsing data – you have probably witnessed this as your web searches follow you around relentlessly in the form of irritating advertisements. It is also why ad blockers have become so popular.

'A squirrel dying in front of your house may be more relevant to your interests right now than people dying in Africa'

Mark Zuckerberg, Facebook
Image credit: Maurizio Pesce

However, profiled filtering has a significant downside. We see the world through a filter bubble leading to confirmation bias: as the browser window through which we see the world progressively tailors itself to our world-view, so our world-view is influenced by what we see.

As a result, we become more separated from information that disagrees with our worldview. By its very subtlety, this is an insidious and damaging trend. In the words of Eli Pariser, political and internet activist,

Eli Pariser
Image credit: The Knight Foundation

'Left to their own devices, personalisation filters serve up a kind of invisible auto propaganda, indoctrinating us with our own ideas, amplifying our desire for things that are familiar and leaving us oblivious to the dangers lurking in the dark territory of the unknown.'

It demands incredible vigilance to counter.

It's not just auto propaganda though. The scope for ordinary propaganda grows every day. November 2016 saw Project Voco unveiled at the Adobe Max conference. Give it 20 minutes of recorded speech and the software will let you create complete phrases and voiceovers as though spoken by the contributor, although the exact words were never actually recorded. This has given birth to the expression 'Sound shopping' (a variation on the theme of 'Photoshopping' as a verb). Tools like this open up a darker side to media manipulation, making it hard for audiences to distinguish between what's real and fake. Put this alongside tools like the experimental Face2Face application developed at Stanford University. While still a prototype, the project explores 'facial reenactment' which facilitates the superimposition of facial movements from one person to another via video. No doubt amateur media producers will soon have the ability to create an entirely fake video.

Both these applications aren't yet commercially available, but there's little doubt that democratised, affordable media production tools with current Hollywood production values isn't far off.

Our challenge in the post-truth world is that networks sharing ever richer content need stronger tools to verify and screen media authenticity.

Face2Face: Real-time Face Capture and Reenactment of RGB Videos.
Thank you to Matthias Niessner of Stanford University for his permission to use this clip. Details of the project partners are contained in the opening of the video.

See futuristmatt.com/fonvideos
Hybrid book users: Video 13

Note from project owners: This demo video is purely research-focused and we would like to clarify the goals and intent of our work. Our aim is to demonstrate the capabilities of modern computer vision and graphics technology, and convey it in an approachable and fun way. We want to emphasize that computer-generated videos have been part in feature-film movies for over 30 years. Virtually every high-end movie production contains a significant percentage of synthetically-generated content (from Lord of the Rings to Benjamin Button). These results are hard to distinguish from reality and it often goes unnoticed that the content is not real. The novelty and contribution of our work is that we can edit pre-recorded videos in real-time on a commodity PC. Please also note that our efforts include the detection of edits in video footage in order to verify a clip's authenticity. For additional information, we refer to our project website (see above). Hopefully, you enjoyed watching our video, and we hope to provide a positive takeaway :)

We need a broadening, challenging worldview if we are to progress and become more tolerant and understanding. Especially when making sense of the future, an ability to question our own prejudice and be exposed to taboos will be critical in our work. Equally, if we are to profitably encourage innovation in our businesses, we must avoid the herd and challenge the status quo by following paths that are less travelled.

Thankfully, there is hope in the form of a technological backlash. For example, the DuckDuckGo search engine does not track usage. There is also a significant groundswell of consumer opinion against filtered intermediation from brands. In February 2016, Twitter launched a mediated stream to replace its timeline – and has been roundly condemned by its user base. Above all, though, we owe it to our personal judgement to expose ourselves to contrary opinions, to learn new skills outside of our usual scope in order to keep our questioning and learning ability fresh. We need to continue to meet people offline, in real-world situations, to expose ourselves to the nuances of genuine human opinion.

Video: Laurent Haug on Filter Bubbles - The Real Problem and Solution.

See futuristmatt.com/fonvideos
Hybrid book users: Video 14

If we are to believe filter bubbles played a large role in the Brexit vote and Trump ascendancy, we need to also take personal responsibility. For the most part, the Facebook algorithm only serves content from people, groups or pages we've already connected with (the exception being sponsored content). As users, we can choose to 'like' or subscribe to sources we may not even feel comfortable with. For example, I didn't agree with a lot of what Donald Trump said

www.duckduckgo.com

during his election campaign, but I did make an effort to subscribe to the material his campaign put out. It's in the interests of online networks to serve us content it thinks we want. After all, their money comes from learning our preferences and selling our details to advertisers. That's fine – it's the deal we make for receiving the services they offer us, free of charge.

It's up to us to counteract this by being aware of how the system works and being proactive to avoid our world-views becoming too narrow.

☹ CRIME

It's already possible for anyone to produce quite sophisticated graphic design using tools like Canva and Typorama. One area we explored in the media section was the growth of more easily usable, yet sophisticated, tools for manipulating the human voice and image. Based on what's happened in graphic design, it's very likely these audio-visual tools will enable anyone to manipulate rich media too. How will we know what truth looks like in a manipulated multimedia world?

Sometimes it's hard to know who to trust, and that's why, in 'Physical to Cyber Crime,' we discover alarming rates of fraud in the UK. Crime is increasingly moving online and policing it is becoming more difficult. The Internet of Things (IoT) is only set to grow the trend in online crime, and the security organisations set up to fight it. But the lines are grey. Activists and non-state actors such as Edward Snowden are accused of treason. Yet, to some, they are heroes.

In 'Terrorism,' we see how groups are moving beyond single issue campaigns to become 'supranational.' As you would expect, the threats are increasingly moving away from 'bullets and bombs' and turning to 'bits and bytes'. Think less the complexity of hijacking planes and more the hugely disruptive and hard-to-trace wiping of financial records.

As terrorists become more sophisticated, so must the counter-terrorism set up to fight it.

PHYSICAL TO CYBER CRIME

How individuals and gangs are capitalising on connectedness to manipulate minds and money – and how traditional policing is struggling to keep up

Physical to Cyber Crime

For many years, crime and its detection operated in the physical realm. Police across the world are better practised at investigating and bringing to justice traditional criminals. But crime-fighting when the criminals' weapons are viruses and codes, is another matter entirely. One of the earliest reported cases of computer crime goes back to 1973. Roswell Steffen, a bank clerk from New York, was found guilty of embezzling US $1.5 million by altering bank account data in the mainframe computer. But Steffen is an anomaly. It was only 26 years ago that computer crime was even recognised with its own category (it was classified as a form of fraud). And only the UK Computer Misuse Act of 1990 started the legal process of codifying so-called 'cyber crime.'

This was in fact remarkably prescient: computer misuse in 1990 was still a case of tweaking private networks, and few people had the opportunity to do this. Little could the authorities know that within a decade, the web would bring connectivity to the masses and across borders, making hacking a sport for all.

Shifting crime trends

Today, authorities are constantly playing catch-up with cyber criminals and the opportunities to commit digital crime will increase exponentially alongside businesses rushing to connect their products to the IoT. This won't change; indeed the concept of policing the internet is perhaps arcane. The UK Office for National Statistics reported that in 2015, 1 in 10 Britons had been victims of online crimes. At 5.8 million offences, that's well over half of all reported crime. Some retail experts feel that an insurance regime (where crime is just a cost of doing business) rather than attempting resolution, might be a better answer.

Computer Misuse Act 1990: hfuturistmatt.com/fonlinks

Equally, scams are only the tip of the iceberg. The breadth of computer crime includes cyber terrorism, industrial sabotage (such as Stuxnet – the supposedly joint US–Israeli computer worm designed to be a cyber weapon) and piracy, along with the many consumer-facing scams like advance fee and chargeback frauds, or the current insidious trend, ransomware. Less publicised but just as important is the social differential of cyber crime. Older people are particularly vulnerable, and hard-pressed law enforcement communities are ill-equipped to help them. There is also a rich seam of romance frauds which may be funny to the well-informed, but are in fact again an abuse of the vulnerable.

A perfect storm of trends is fuelling digital crime. This includes an exponentially increasing number of devices, internet connections and bandwidth; classic crimes moving online; the changing nature of software makes it difficult to build robust defences; the fact that a large amount of damage can be caused very quickly by a single attack; and that attackers are very hard to identify.

Indeed, many so-called 'classic crimes' are moving online (e.g. from fraud to phishing) because it is easier and more scalable to run a scam through the internet than it is to try and burgle a bank. Also, online crime is faceless, often perceived by many as digital and therefore victimless. It is also still very much 'white collar,' therefore the criminals who perpetrate it do not, perhaps, feel the same level of culpability or 'fear factor' as they might when running the risk of coming directly into contact with the arm of the law.

Although there are numerous firewalls and types of anti-virus software out there, it is almost impossible for these to give the user complete safety as things are constantly changing. Generally, the software ope-

UK

Hacked and leaked data from online infidelity site 'Ashley Madison' visualised via Google maps. In the UK, the highest number of site users were from Wimbledon, London. Credit: **Malfideleco.**

Ashley Madison: futuristmatt.com/fonlinks

GhostSec: futuristmatt.com/fonlinks

rates on a minimum viable product basis to remain profitable; in other words, launch first and fix later. Even top manufacturers are patching and enhancing as they go. Similarly, the threat landscape is never static: cyber security is a trench war of many individual battles.

While there may be many individual battles, cyber crime can operate at scale. Although fixes can be rolled out quickly, a single attacker can have a magnified effect by affecting many users in seconds.

Access the deep web via
www.torproject.org

A forensic investigation in 2016 revealed how an electricity blackout in western Ukraine occurred due to a sustained attack on the utility provider. To further compound the difficulties, attribution is exceptionally hard – an eleven-year-old in a cyber café is often as well resourced as state actors. You only need download a 'TOR' browser to explore hacking forums on the deep web to realise this.

We live in a post-Westphalian age – an explosion of globalisation, in which physical borders are more porous, but our virtual borders have to all intents and purposes evaporated completely. Indeed some of the most interesting digital confrontations are between non-state privateers. GhostSec, an offshoot of the libertarian digital activist group, Anonymous, is a self-described vigilante group formed to attack ISIS websites that promote Islamic extremism.

Another non-state digital privateer of note is, of course, Edward Snowden. Like Anonymous, his actions attract either praise or revulsion: he is either a free speech hero or a traitor to civilised society. Whichever side of the free speech divide you sit on, perhaps the most

Anonymous: futuristmatt.com/fonlinks

important fact is that Snowden is one man; the subsequent leak of the Panama Papers – certainly not a large group effort – shows that individuals and small groups have immense power to leverage change in the digital world.

Traditional policing will continue to find challenging cyber crime hard. It will have to concentrate on major frauds where the opportunity for redress warrants investigation. They will also be permanently behind the technological curve.

However, the technical challenge is less significant than the real issue, which is whether legislation and cross-border agreements can keep up with the changing nature of computer crime.

TERRORISM

How motivated interest groups are moving away from 'bullets and bombs' and turning to 'bits and bytes' to disrupt the social order from a bedroom

Terrorism

As the well-worn phrase has it, 'One man's terrorist is another man's freedom fighter.' We also often hear the phrase, 'history is written by the victors', as those with power mould the ongoing narrative of countries and governments, and decide which groups are characterised in any particular way.

For the purposes of this discussion, this is my definition of terrorism: 'premeditated attacks on members of the public with political goals in mind.' This should be relatively uncontentious and allows us to avoid taking political sides. Importantly, it also pointedly avoids any discussion of scale: the micro-cells of the IRA or Baader-Meinhof are very different from the large groups emerging from failed states which are almost indistinguishable from armies.

Indeed, across the board, terrorist groups are developing new capabilities and becoming more efficient in their attacks. They are moving from taking a subordinate role in nation-state conflicts to becoming international influencers in their own right. For example, the Chilcot Report has, among many other things, shown that the British Army in its Iraq campaign was forced to negotiate a prisoner exchange with a local militia of no formal army standing. As connected commercialised entities, they are also becoming more integrated with sub-state organisations such as criminal networks and legitimate corporations.

Che Guevara – Terrorist or Freedom Fighter?
Credit: **Jim Fitzpatrick / Wikimedia Commons**

Increasingly, terror groups are taking decentralisation to its logical limit. Al-Qaeda (founded by Osama Bin Laden) was just one of the groups widely reported to be using the standard clandestine cell structure, popularised throughout history. Within these networks, information on leadership is restricted – with senior figures often known only as 'Commander.' But the internet, other communications and security options mean that cells can be far more practically resourced without traditional contact. Al-Qaeda operations would be decided by leadership but managed locally. Logistics support such as forged documents, hiding places, communication, transportation, information, arms and ammunition could be easily provided at scale by other cells as needed.

As terror groups have outgrown the single-issue or local operation, they have often become supranational; meaning their ambitions are truly global. When did you last hear about Peru's 'Shining Path' or Italy's 'Red Brigade'? Neither achieve more than a blip in the global media narrative. Rather, especially with the supportive impetus of religious justification, major terror groups create locally relevant narratives

on a global stage. However, they continue to use similarly localised and practical ways to raise revenue, from drugs and protection racketeering through to semi-legitimised appropriation of the machinery of state.

This reach also powers so-called 'home-grown extremism.' In April 2015, EU Justice Minister Věra Jourová stated that 5,000–6,000 Europeans had ventured to fight with ISIS in Syria. A major fear for governments across the EU is that Jihadi fighters return to carry out atrocities in their home countries.

We've seen it already: Mehdi Nemmouche, a French national, killed four people at the Jewish Museum in Brussels in 2014 after spending a year fighting with ISIS in Syria. According to a leaked document by Belgium's anti-terror unit, fighters leaving Syria are re-entering Europe through countries like Turkey and Greece, often hiding among legitimate refugees to avoid detection. Al-Qaeda members usually carried Middle Eastern passports; ISIS members are just as likely to have European identities.

But who needs a passport when you can wreak far more havoc online? According to Cyber War written by Richard A. Clarke and Robert K. Knake, there is enormous potential disruption in:

- **AFFECTING NATIONAL TRAIN NETWORKS – CAUSING HORRIFIC ACCIDENTS AND REDUCING FREEDOM OF MOVEMENT AND GOODS**
- **DAMAGING ELECTRICAL GRIDS**
- **WIPING FINANCIAL RECORDS, PREVENTING ANYONE FROM KNOWING WHO OWNS WHAT AND BADLY DAMAGING THE FINANCIAL SYSTEM**
- **WIPING MEDICAL RECORDS, MAKING DIAGNOSIS AND TREATMENT OF CRITICAL PATIENTS DIFFICULT AND DANGEROUS**

Clarke and Knake point out that while government military and intelligence networks are comparatively well protected, the private sector is often woefully inadequate when it comes to security measures to protect themselves.

Technology has also given terrorists the tools to create media easily, allowing them to engage not only with targets for radicalisation or controlled communities but also to cut across cultural barriers. As US Secretary of State, Martin Dempsey said, 'Victory against the Islamic State will not be achieved through the military. Instead, their ability to spread their ideas must be stopped.'

The tools available for production and distribution are getting better and cheaper every day. As President Obama warned, 'The high-quality videos, the online magazines, the use of social media, terrorist Twitter accounts – it's all designed to target today's young people online, in cyberspace.' There was even a Twitter application, 'Fajr-al-Bashaer' ('Dawn of Good Tidings') that sent updates about fighting in Syria and Iraq. It's particularly smart as, once users signed up, it

Middle East Research Institute: futuristmatt.com/fonlinks

sent automated, staggered updates via subscribers' accounts to their followers. By staggering updates, it avoided detection by anti-spam software.

Propaganda like the Dawn of Glad Tidings app from ISIS will surely evolve alongside technology

The nature of content is also changing. In The West, we often believe the bulk of ISIS content to be violent executions of aid workers, journalists, a Jordanian pilot, etc. But Elliot Zweig of the Middle East Research Institute notes, 'You see messages of camaraderie.' It is not all difficulty and gore and suffering. 'It is "come and join us, join me and we'll fight the good fight together."' It softens the core message of Jihad and is much more inviting to frustrated, disaffected Westerners looking for a sense of purpose.

So where next? As communication channels become ever more ubiquitous, so will the nefariousness and sophistication of terror groups. Uncensored videos such as these at 'Zero Censorship' can be copied and shared infinitely, globally, in seconds. In terrorism, just as in business, barriers to entry will continue to get lower. As the cost of drones continues to drop, expect the rise of lone wolf types carrying homemade explosives, the recipes for which were freely available online (or via the dark web). Soon the need to risk terrorist lives will disappear. John McAfee points out that modern 'fly by wire' planes could be subject to digital hijackings. And what of self-driving cars? I'll leave that

Dawn of Glad Tidings: futuristmatt.com/fonlinks

Zero Censorship: futuristmatt.com/fonlinks

to your imagination! Also, let's not ignore the 30 billion connected devices (IoT) forecast by 2020 – the more the web grows, the more vulnerable it becomes.

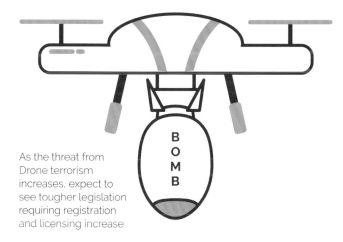

As the threat from Drone terrorism increases, expect to see tougher legislation requiring registration and licensing increase

One thing's for sure. It will always be a cat-and-mouse game between authorities and terrorists. Counter-terrorism detection is getting more sophisticated too. It's widely known that authorities monitor citizens' calls, emails, etc. and are slowly probing into VoIP (Voice over Internet Protocol) and even virtual worlds. Then, the EU is also funding the HUMABIO (Human Monitoring and Authentication using Biodynamic Indicators and Behavioural Analysis) project. In addition to fingerprinting and voice recognition, HUMABIO is in the nascent stages of attempting to scan our brain stems. Could technology like this be the next frontier in airport security? The programme has even published its own ethics manual. As biometric checks become increasingly sophisticated, they will learn more about us in seconds than our friends could find out in years.

To leave you with the sobering reality that we may face: 'Technological advances could allow a rogue regime, terrorists or criminal groups to synthesise highly contagious, fatal viruses with long incubation periods that would make early detection and quarantine very difficult. The promise of an anti-virus could be used to extort money, goods or used for political leverage. It is even possible that viruses could, in future, be engineered to target specific individuals or groups, making them a more viable weapon.' If you'd like to dig further, check out the report from the UK's Ministry of Defence 'Global Strategic Trends – Out to 2045.'

While we'll see new forms of terrorism, there'll be new jobs to combat it. I can't say what the jobs will be, but expect to see a surge in demand for skills around data science, transport infrastructure development, and anything surveillance related.

And for sure, the future is more 'bits and bytes' than 'bullets and bombs.'

🚀 TECHNOLOGY

In the previous section, we explored how criminal and terrorist acts are increasingly taking place in the sphere of technology. We are now seeing new technology paradigms emerge, all of which are open to criminal abuse, but also more legitimate uses.

In 'Augmented Reality,' we look at how the world is being supplemented by additional information layers provided by our smart devices. You're in for a treat when watching Keiichi Matsuda's 'Hyper-Reality' short film. Its dystopian view presents you with a vision of a day in the life like you've never seen before.

In 'Virtual Reality,' we'll explore how VR is nothing new – its roots go back to early mechanical flight simulators. VR opportunities abound in areas such as surgical training, entertainment, fundraising and more. If it does take off, there's an ethical dimension to be considered too.

And finally, in 'Artificial Intelligence,' we go all the way from Alan Turing, AI domination and Universal Basic Income, to the technological singularity, where AI usurps us as well as our ability to comprehend it. We also look at instances when AI is added to robots.

Technology is the perfect place to end as it encompasses so much of what we have already looked at and affects every aspect of business, work, society and media.

AUGMENTED REALITY

How we can marshal information
into our fields of vision and experience,
both to solve problems or, of course,
for a whole new marketing opportunity

Pokemon GO: futuristmatt.com/fonlinks

Augmented Reality

There's a lot of talk in marketing circles about the potential for Augmented Reality (AR). Unlike its more totally immersive cousin, Virtual Reality (VR), AR creates new layers of experience over what we already see in the real world. AR is 'a live direct or indirect view of a physical, real-world environment whose elements are augmented (or supplemented) by computer-generated sensory input such as sound, video, graphics or GPS data.' Many will be familiar with it in the form of Pokémon GO, a 2016 phenomenon in which users would use their mobile devices to locate and capture Pokémon.

AR differs from the VR experience by using information or communicating further meaning onto the real-world experience. Future tourists may walk around Stonehenge and have reading matter piped into view according to where they look. Equally, having your field of vision bathed in red for an emergency situation is something every gamer understands, and which is another great example of AR communication.

My mind was blown by a short, crowdfunded film created by Keiichi Matsuda. Matsuda says: *'Our physical and virtual realities are becoming increasingly intertwined. Technologies such as VR, augmented reality, wearables, and the internet of things are pointing to a*

Hyper Reality / **Credit: Keeichi Matsuda**

world where technology will envelop every aspect of our lives. It will be the glue between every interaction and experience, offering amazing possibilities, while also controlling the way we understand the world. Hyper-Reality attempts to explore this exciting but dangerous trajectory. It was crowdfunded, and shot on location in Medellin, Colombia.'

His video takes the 'selfie' age and magnifies it. It shows how AR puts the individual at the centre of their own universe as the ultimate expression of personalisation. But this isn't necessarily a good thing. You'll notice the point at which the system reboots, showing a drab, colourless supermarket. The danger lies in how AR could add to an already increasing feeling of isolation. If children grow up in an AR environment such as that painted by Matsuda, will they want to be present in the non-augmented world? The social, ethical and legal issues presented are astonishing and are ripe for a book unto themselves.

Video: 'Keiichi Matsuda – Hyper Reality'.

See futuristmatt.com/fonvideos
Hybrid book users: Video 15

If you've used VR technologies, you'll know they're both stimulating but also thoroughly exhausting, as the range of stimulation is diverse and intense. That said, my experience was nothing like this world-view, as presented by Matsuda. If you're curious what a hyper-accelerated augmented world could look like, I strongly advise you to spend 6 minutes of your life on this. I wouldn't be surprised if you watch it several times – there's a lot to take in.

You'll have to watch it yourself to see what this scene is all about!

Above all, this video demonstrates the importance of maintaining our mindfulness under the assault of a world of increasingly layered complexity.

That said, if you're reading this book, you're the one stepping gingerly into virtual worlds. Future generations will find themselves immersed in them from birth and presumably will find their brains adapt accordingly.

While we might struggle to adjust to these new environments, perhaps our children's children will struggle in a different way, when their worlds reboot – or even go offline.

VIRTUAL
REALITY

How entirely new worlds are revolutionising entertainment and education but also challenge what it means to live, work and participate in social experiences

Link Trainer: futuristmatt.com/fonlinks

Virtual Reality

Most of us love words as they let us conjure up ideas in the imagination. I remember well the telling of campfire horror stories as a Boy Scout. The storyteller had us on the edge of our logs, and none of us slept comfortably for days afterwards. It was exhilarating and terrifying at the same time! That said, words can be quite a crude way of making a point. Their meaning can only be as detailed as the definitions the receiver attaches to them; and there is plenty of room for misinterpretation, whether through nuance or linguistic differences.

For centuries, we have used words to teach, but Virtual Reality (VR) offers us the chance to literally show others what we mean. It can remove the ambiguity of words by providing all parties with the same information, in an immediate way. Instead of teachers 'describing,' students will be able to 'experience.' Learning can become a first-person activity instead of a second-hand one. That said, it's only as good as its programmers, and we should be mindful of the fact it's still a filtered version of our realities.

VR is nothing new. To find the world's first flight simulator, we have to go all the way back to a mechanical marvel of 1929. Called the 'Link Trainer' after its inventor, Edwin Link, it presented pilots with instrumentation and even moved appropriately according to how the controls were handled. Pulling up, diving, banking – it was all possible. The Link Trainer is the first example of something approaching a genuinely immersive experience.

The Link Trainer mechanical flight simulator
Credit: BZUK / Wikimedia Commons

View Master: futuristmatt.com/fonlinks

Oculus Rift: futuristmatt.com/fonlinks

If you grew up in the 1970s and 80s, you have probably used a View-Master toy (still very much available, but as you might expect, significantly evolved!). A headset using the now commonplace differentiated views for left and right eyes which creates the illusion of a 3D space, these were originally military tools for training pilots and gunners in the range estimation of target planes and ships. The first head-mounted system as we'd recognise it today began development in 1966 at MIT's Lincoln Laboratory. It was so heavy it had to be suspended from a ceiling. It was humorously known as the 'Sword of Damocles' – perhaps a foreboding sign of things to come?

The classic Viewmaster

Sword of Damocles: futuristmatt.com/fonlinks

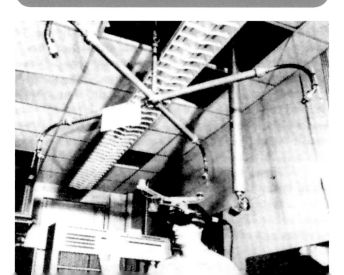

Bringing VR to the modern day, we see Facebook's acquisition of VR specialist, Oculus (and its product, the Rift), back in 2014 for $2 billion. Mark Zuckerberg is betting big on headsets that provide immersive 3D experiences; yes that's movies and television, but also tools for business meetings and gaming. No doubt his ultimate goal is headsets that scan our brains then transmit thoughts to friends in the way we share humorous cat pictures and videos today.

The 'Sword of Damocles'
– you wouldn't want this to
fall on you head!

Thought sharing - Future of Facebook?

Why is Zuckerberg betting big on VR? Because he wants presence. We have tools like Skype and Slack which can be the cornerstone of distributed work teams and allow us to connect with people across any distance. But once our brains believe on some level that we're in the same space as others, that's when we'll replicate the offline benefits of spontaneous interaction and that all important non-verbal communication. In short, we will communicate more freely and effectively, because more of the problems of technology – poor user interface, lack of realism – have been removed.

Once we've made the virtual world real, we can also make it better. The next step in VR is multiple or selectable realities. This could mean elegant and simple benefits like algorithmically enhanced colour schemes to improve the experience for colour blind people. Or it could mean a more sinister world in which brands penetrate our every waking moment.

Then there's robotics. Returning to the flight simulator, robotics have been used for a realistic VR experience since the 1950s; their improved precision and flexibility mean that robots are sure to be the hands and feet of the VR experience. Advances in surgical training will definitely take advantage of VR. It reduces reliance on human cadavers and animals while allowing trainees to easily fail and repeat techniques. During one study of surgical residents, those who undertook VR simulation of gall bladder surgery were 6 times less likely to make errors and 29% faster than those who did not participate in the training. Moving beyond training, we already have tools like da Vinci surgery. Combine this with VR and surgeons will soon be able to 'get inside' an organ to see detail previously unavailable. Not a bad step on the journey towards nanobot surgery, where tiny robots will work inside our bodies.

da Vinci surgery: futuristmatt.com/fonlinks

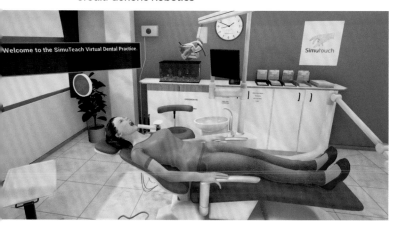

First person view from the Simuteach Dental VR training application.
Credit: Generic Robotics

Professor Jeremy Bailenson, Stanford: futuristmatt.com/fonlinks

their VR devices every half hour. People often report nausea, eyestrain and headaches. Professor Jeremy Bailenson of Stanford University makes a case for VR affecting how a user thinks and behaves. Indeed, a teacher friend of mine recently told me (on a lesser level) that she witnessed one of her 6-year-olds trying to 'swipe' the tank at the aquarium. The child's mind has been conditioned to believe that anything behind glass is virtual. The same sort of thought patterns will no doubt become evident in VR situations, especially for those born and brought up once VR is commonplace.

It is fair to say that VR opportunities for commerce have barely begun to be realised. You can already explore IKEA kitchens and no doubt you'll soon be able to see how that shelf unit looks in the corner of the living room. In cosmetics, you can try 10 lipsticks in the time it takes to do one. Sephora makes it possible. Online shopping will certainly take on a new dimension!

It's not all good, though, and we must take heed of precautions with regard to VR. Both Samsung and Oculus advise adults to take 10-minute breaks from

Fish in aquariums don't respond to glass swiping

Simuteach: futuristmatt.com/fonlinks

W.M. Keck Center: futuristmatt.com/fonlinks

Lady playing VR game 'The Climb' on an Oculus Rift.
Credit: Marco Verch / Wikimedia Commons

Meanwhile, recent studies of lab rats at the W. M. Keck Center for Neurophysics at UCLA revealed abnormal patterns of activity in rat brains, including 60% of neurone shut down in VR environments. What's not understood, however, is whether this is a good or bad thing in the context of the experiment. Then, there's the cost. VR currently takes significant financial investment to develop a virtual environment. That said, I've no doubt it'll follow the same path as web development, with plug-and-play modules becoming the norm.

Having tried Oculus Rift myself as part of a group, one thing struck me. Everyone starts wondering how VR will change the future in their particular field. A sculptor in the group got excited by the opportunities that simply wouldn't have been possible before. A Formula 1 fan said they'd love to be in the pit lane as the cars came in for tyre changes. One lady from a well-known charity remarked how effective it would be to bring alive the struggles of the people they help. In her words, 'the potential for fundraising is incredible.'

However, there's so much more to understand. There are clearly incredible opportunities, but also significant risks. As haptic (the use of the sense of touch) technology becomes the norm, will we even leave the house? Or will digital detoxing become essential for us to re-adjust to 'real' reality? Like any technology, VR has pros and cons, but unlike most technologies, VR can amplify the human experience beyond all expectations.

If you're the Dalai Lama, experiences can create empathy and drive human connection. If you're Donald Trump, experiences can spread hate and fear. Both angles take the viewer out of their own universe and plunge them completely into another.

The ethical dimension never goes away and never should.

ARTIFICIAL INTELLIGENCE

How robotics, algorithms and knowledge as a utility will affect, enhance or even usurp society as we know it

Artificial Intelligence

Artificial Intelligence, commonly referred to as 'AI,' is the science and engineering of making intelligent machines. While it has become an increasingly familiar term, its roots lie with Alan Turing. He led the team which famously cracked the Enigma code machine used by Nazis during the Second World War to pass secret communications. In 1950, he created what is now called the 'Turing Test,' which is still used as a means of determining whether a machine can effectively pass itself off as a human.

Alan Turing at 16. Widely considered to be the father of Artificial Intelligence.
Credit: Turing Archive / Wikimedia Commons.

Despite a few hype cycles, often referred to as 'AI winters' when funding for AI is reduced, expectations set by research and the reality it actually delivers are beginning to align. Aside from the behemoths like Apple, Facebook, Amazon and Google all ploughing vast sums into research, the landscape for start-ups continues to grow. In 2011, there were roughly 70 AI related start-ups that had achieved significant funding. That figure hit nearly 400 by the end of 2015. By the close of 2016, this number rose to nearly 600.

It was widely reported in 2016 that DeepMind's AlphaGo program (owned by Google) had beaten the 18-time world champion Lee Se-dol at the game of Go. The significance of this cannot be underestimated as it was previously presumed a computer couldn't beat a human champion due to the preconceived idea that Go is a game of intuition. While the rules are straightforward, the game has more potential positions than atoms in the universe – and therefore winning requires the ability to 'think' strategically. This victory is a step change in the way AI is perceived. I would, however, still argue that it is nowhere near assuming human qualities. The machine wasn't happy,

Alan Turing: futuristmatt.com/fonlinks

Deepmind: futuristmatt.com/fonlinks

had no one to share its £1 million winnings with and simply did what it was programmed to do.

Winning at Go is not the end game, of course. The big players recognise that products and services are moving away from 'form' or 'app' interfaces to a more conversational approach. Facebook's DeepText is set to understand thousands of messages per second and in over 20 languages. Amazon's deal with Angel. ai in September 2016 opened the doors for it to automate customer service via chatbots. Customers will be able to interact with the brand using natural language and get services automatically rather than requiring a human to make decisions.

Some of us are already using 'weak AI' on our smartphones. Siri, Google Now and Cortana are all spoken-word digital assistants operating on iOS, Android and Windows Mobile. The research firm, Gartner, predicts that by 2020, 30% of all web-browsing sessions will be conducted without a screen, using voice search only. Another notable statistic from Gartner is that by 2019, 20% of brands will abandon their mobile apps. AI will be the key facilitator as the step-change towards 'chat' based services at scale is predicated on it.

Vladimir and Estragon Google Home digital assistants having a conversation together in January 2017.
Credit: Twitch / Seebotschat

Nature: futuristmatt.com/fonlinks

Blue Tesla charging in the Netherla
Credit: David van der Mark / Wikimedia Comm

Moving into the physical realm, expect to see AI growth in areas such as self-driving cars. A key development is how the algorithms learn. In 2015, the scientific journal, Nature, published research demonstrating how DeepMind had created a programme which was able to master Atari's Space Invaders game. Rather than being given a set of rules, it was simply given an objective – to achieve the highest score possible. Through repeated attempts, it achieved superhuman results. In other words, it won through experience.

This matters for self-driving cars as, instead of pro-gramming maps, traffic lights or positions of obsta-cles, algorithms could play out billions of scenarios in a virtual environment, learning all the time and only then moving on to physical tests. Certainly not self-aware, but they could learn from experience rather than pure programming. A key component of this ability to assimilate is the acquisition of huge amounts of real-world data; which is why Tesla, a leader in self-driving cars, sends thousands of parameters from every one of its vehicles back to base, to refine its algorithms automatically.

Despite all this, there are still serious weaknesses to be overcome. For example, if the onboard cameras are blinded by sunlight, they could fail to spot a chan-ging traffic light. Sensors are as yet unable to reco-gnise certain road obstacles. Humans find it easy to differentiate a lump of stone from a cardboard box, but machines don't. The potential for a dangerous, unneeded swerve remains.

Tesla: futuristmatt.com/fonlinks

So how will AI influence our lives going forward? If we believe science fiction, not very well. *2001: A Space Odyssey, The Matrix and The Terminator, Ex Machina* all paint rather dystopian pictures. They fit into two broad categories:

- Dominance: Robots control humanity, resulting in us being submissive or under threat of extinction.
- Rebellion: AI becomes self-aware and attempts to destroy us.

Sci-fi aficionados will remember the iconic 'Hal 9000' from the film Space Odyssey without prompting.
Credit: Grafiker61 / Wikimedia Commons

My sense is that we tend towards anthropomorphising. That is to say, we imbue AI with human characteristics – including the idea that a sentient AI will either love us or hate us. This assumes that self-aware machines would have human value systems, which seems unlikely. There is, however, a mood amongst well known luminaries such as Stephen Hawking, Elon Musk (CEO of Tesla) and others that AI will doom us.

One thing is clear – AI will change the world. As we saw in how the future of work is going to change, machines are already having an early impact on jobs. Those jobs that can be automated should be automated, displacing millions of workers. Optimists love to proselytise how machines will create an abundance of near costless goods and services. In June 2016, Switzerland conducted the first referendum on Universal Basic Income (UBI). Citizens were asked to vote on a proposal that everyone should receive a guaranteed basic income. Although it failed, supporters argue that as work is increasingly automated, fewer jobs are available. Expect to see much more about UBI as societies look for ways to deal with AI doing more of its work.

Universal Basic Income: futuristmatt.com/fonlinks

The Technological Singularity: futuristmatt.com/fonlinks

Looking further ahead, we see AI merging into a state of technological singularity. Notable futurists such as Ray Kurzweil describe this as the point where exponential improvements in technologies such as genetics, nanotechnology, robotics, AI and computers reach a point where 'progress is so rapid it outstrips humans' ability to comprehend it.' According to Kurzweil, this will arrive in 2045, though this prediction is widely disputed. My sense is that we've reached a crossroads. In the short term, AI offers us fantastic opportunities for commerce and enriching our lives through better products and services. Where it becomes murkier, is that technological developments are largely uncontrolled and unpredictable. As systems become more interconnected, they have the potential to learn from one another. That's where things get very uncertain. My natural inclination is to remain optimistic though as we look forward to advances in disease elimination, surgical robots with precision control, the reduction of poverty and much more.

For me, a utopian mid-term future is one where AI-powered robots augment humans. Robots have already demonstrated their usefulness in repeatable tasks. Just visit any mass car manufacturer to see that. In the previous section about supply chains, we saw how robots like Baxter are being trained to act as 'Pick/Pack' robots. There's a lot of debate about what will happen as AI and robotics get smarter and what it means for humanity. I would argue humans will get smarter too as we gain a greater understanding of genetics and redress the man/machine balance.

Video: 'Dr Trudy Barber on AI and Sex Robots'.
See futuristmatt.com/fonvideos
Hybrid book users: Video 16

Velociraptor greets hotel guest
Credit: Hen na hotel

While robots have acted behind the scenes for years, we're finally starting to see them in our everyday lives. Back in 2015, we saw the opening of the first robot-powered hotel in Japan. On arrival, guests are greeted and checked in by either a humanoid lady who speaks Japanese or, slightly bizarrely, an English-speaking Velociraptor. Gone are the days of the keycard. Check-in includes taking a photograph of your face, which becomes the digital image granting access to rooms through facial recognition technology. There's even a robot cloakroom where a robot arm stores and retrieves your valuables in a bank of locked boxes.

However, the service is not completely automated. While the robot porters will transport luggage to your room, they can't summon a taxi or recommend local attractions. And the hotel still employs human security guards and staff to clean and make the beds. They're also present to deal with emergencies, of course. The ambition of Hena Na (or Weird Hotel) is to have the hotel fully automated in order to keep costs low and profits high.

Hen na's logical extraction of costs suggests that wealthy people – or even many ordinary people – in the future will likely pay a premium to maintain personal interactions. The human touch will be a prime differentiator; consumers will pay more to access human doctors, receptionists, fitness coaches, babysitters and more.

Robot cloakroom in action
Credit Hen na hotel

Human service comes at a premium price.

Universal Robots: futuristmatt.com/fonlinks

In some cases, this will signify quality – as with a hotel. In other cases, it will represent the premium value of a bespoke service – a human fitness coach will be instinctively more tailored than a digital motivator. And in others, it represents nothing more than tradition. There is, for example, plenty of evidence that digital doctors will be far more effective at identifying and triaging symptoms in patients, but many will still want the personal touch of a gentle bedside manner, even if the level of professional service is actually not as good.

In the business world, Betty is pioneering the way for robots to work as your office manager. Don't underestimate Betty's crude appearance for being dumb. She greets guests and staff, tracks employee hours and overtime and manages the ordering of office materials. She can also navigate around the office, so can escort guests to meeting rooms. And you'd better not 'permanently borrow' stationery for home or she'll know it's missing!

So what do robots mean for us? Even in 2013, Oxford academics Dr Carl Benedikt and Michael Osborne predicted that around 47% of all jobs in the US would probably become automated. Those safest in the short to mid-term included artists, clergy and teachers. Those most at risk included accountants, cashiers, telemarketers and sports referees. There is also scope to share the workload – take a doctor as an example. The actual diagnosis and treatment could perhaps be done better by machine, but the human skills of empathy and an emotional understanding could still be done by a person.

Meet Betty – The Future of Office Robots?
Credit: University of Birmingham

Betty the Robot: futuristmatt.com/fonlinks

There's little doubt robots will play a more important role in society. In some cases, they will take over existing jobs. Look at the multitasker bot from Momentum Machines: it can make and flip a burger in 10 seconds flat. Not long till the McDonalds crew gets replaced! Universal Robots have a manufacturing device that even builds new parts for itself when they need replacing while Google has a patent to build worker robots with personalities. I only hope they don't suffer from mental illness – I really don't want to deal with a sandwich making bot that throws the ingredients at me!

If history is anything to go by, the future is positive. The economy has changed, and people are generally better off. In the nineteenth century, 4 out of 5 people worked on the land to produce food. Now, it's less than 2% (US) and 1.5% (UK). Food is more abundant and cheaper than ever, which means that many people can afford to spend time and money on other pursuits. We automated blue collar work; people transitioned. We're automating white collar work; people will transition. I hope a future exists where we separate jobs from work. Those things that can be automated should be automated. Even then, robots aren't about to take all our jobs. It is far likelier that they will augment us as they have done, but will do so in more sophisticated ways.

Those things which make us human – empathy, love, understanding – should be developed and celebrated with the new time we hopefully have to pursue them.

SANDWICH

BAR

Hopefully the robot servers won't glitch much or your sandwich shop visit could get very messy!

Conclusion

If there's one lesson I hope you take away from the experience of reading this book, it's the importance of keeping an open mind. Be open in terms of welcoming social and technological evolution as it happens. During the first internet revolution in 1995–2000, some journalists refused to budge from old ways of working. They were the ones who were least prepared for what turned out to be a tidal wave of change, and least equipped to keep their jobs and livelihoods. People with open minds adapt and thrive.

On a related theme, I also invite you to be open in terms of being non-judgemental. Virtually all trends have both good and bad effects. Social science can almost be summed up as the study of unintended consequences. Our electronic devices have made us more connected and yet emotionally drained. The gig economy has brought millions of people into the workplace and yet created inequality. None of these developments is fundamentally good or bad, and it is the duty of us all as informed and inquisitive consumers to make balanced judgements.

I also want to highlight a trend about trends – an übertrend! When I assess the ideas presented in this book as a whole, I sense that future technologies are going to be increasingly organic rather than mechanical. Again, I mean this in more than one way. We should keep our eyes open for developments in biotechnology and its interaction with computer science. I have no doubt that that's where some of the Henry Fords of the future will come from.

But I also think the traditional idea of mechanical invention is largely redundant. Not only is innovation coming from much larger and better-funded teams (our academic institutions, scientific foundations and big business), but there is a social component to innovation too. Ideas 'have their moment' because they are relevant to large markets and consumers play a role in defining what warrants effort. Indeed, the invention is only a component of innovation – to be useful, it requires significant people, process and financial resource to develop and supply.

The mind is as organic as the body, and it's becoming ever more obvious that we need to look after it.

Machines will automate many aspects of our lives, but we will only thrive if we continue to develop the human skills that they find difficult to replicate. Technology makes our lives more convenient than ever, but we must be mindful to maintain and develop our human relationships. We are all realising that no matter how many online friends we have, they are no substitute for healthy, face-to-face relationships. We are flesh and blood, not avatars after all.

I have consciously not put timescales on the trends discussed here. Some are already happening, we are on the cusp of others, and some require both technology and social acceptance to align in miraculous eclipse, to suddenly gain traction. As I mentioned in the introduction, prediction is a fool's errand.

What I can promise is that we live in a time when the rate of change is accelerating exponentially. For me, this is exciting beyond belief, and as discussed above, it brings both positive and negative outcomes. It means that we may, with the right political and social incentives, have the wherewithal to solve the great challenges of our time, such as population growth, care for our aged and climate change. Equally, it means we have huge challenges in our education systems to equip future generations to contribute as workers and to discover fulfilment in their physical and emotional lives.

I hope that you will take new perspectives away from this book which you can use in both your business and daily life and which will inspire you to not just manage the challenges of radical change, but help you to find opportunity at every turn. Accepting that the future is now helps us embrace the positives of change, minimise the negative impacts and be mindful of how technology is shaping our lives.

BUILD YOUR POSITIVE FUTURE!
and get in touch today

Example applications:

- Taking a long-term strategic view; and focusing your resources accordingly
- Developing new sales and marketing plans, discovering new opportunities

- Building the confidence and resilience to escape short-termism
- Developing sound corporate values fit for the 21st century
- Improving customer relevance and quality of service
- Revitalising departments and

teams - creating genuine employee engagement
- Communicating more effectively, both internally and outside the organisation
- Finding ways to recruit the best people – and retain them

Matt works across the world with a range of organisations including Accor Hotels, Avis Budget, British Council, Dialog Semiconductor, Epicor, First Data, Tata, Unilever and many more.

Presentations & Keynotes

Tailored keynote speeches, presentations and immersive discussion sessions, always leaving audiences with actionable ideas that they can take forward in their organisations.

Engaging Teams

Let us help you communicate your ideas, invite input and embed your future change though innovative communication strategies to reach the wider organisation.

Interactive Workshops

Working with you to apply the latest trends to your corporate strategies, creating better products and services, developing new sales and marketing plans and more.

Immersive Events

Futurist.Matt and the EventExtra team are expert at creating playful, inspiring environments in which to make considering the future a fun and enriching experience.

futurist.matt

helping organisations manage their future

Call now:
+44 (0)20 7193 0104

Futurist.Matt

| Media Junction | 2 Archer Street |
London W1D 7AW

Email: matt@futuristmatt.com

For more information:
www.futuristmatt.com

Helping organisations manage their future

Further Reading

The Infinite Resource by Ramez Naam, University Press of New England, 2013

The Responsibility Revolution by Jeffrey Hollender, Wiley, 2010

Think Like a Futurist by Cecily Sommers, Wiley, 2012

The Technological Singularity by Murray Shanahan, MIT Press, 2015

The Future of Business edited by Rohit Talwar, Fast Future Publishing, 2015

Technology vs. Humanity by Gerd Leonhard, Fast Future Publishing, 2016

The Trend Management Toolkit by Anne Lise Kjaer, Palgrave Macmillan, 2014

The Rise of the Robots by Martin Ford, Oneworld Publications, 2016

The Second Machine Age by Erik Brynjolfsson & Andrew McAfee, WW Norton & Co, 2016

Driving Desired Futures edited by Michael Shamiyeh, Birkhauser Verlag AG, 2014

The B Corp Handbook by Ryan Honeyman, EDS Publications, 2014

The Cluetrain Manifesto by Rick Levine et al. (10th anniversary edition), Basic Books, 2011

The Quantified Self by Deborah Lupton, Polity Press, 2016

Cyber War by Richard A. Clarke & Robert K. Knake, Ecco, 2012

The Sharing Economy by Arun Sundararajan, MIT Press, 2016

Multiple Intelligences by Howard Gardner, Basic Books, 2006

Working Out Loud by John Stepper, Ikigai Press, 2015

The End of Leadership by Barbara Kellerman, HarperBusiness, 2012

#Loneliness: The Virus of the Modern Age by Tony Jeton Selimi, BalboaPress, 2016

The Filter Bubble by Eli Pariser, Penguin Books, 2012

Introduction to Cybercrime by Joshua Hill and Nancy Marion, Praeger Security International, 2016

Future Crimes by Marc Goodman, Corgi, 2016

Augmented by Brett King, Marshall Cavendish International, 2016

Flash Boys by Michael Lewis, Penguin, 2015

The Marketing Imagination by Theodore Levitt, Free Press, 1986

Future Food (Kindle Edition) by Aaron Council & Michael Petch, Gyges 3D Presents, 2015

The Gig Economy by Diane Mulcahy, AMACOM, 2016

The Fourth Industrial Revolution by Klaus Schwab, World Economic Forum, 2016

This book wouldn't have been possible
without the help and support of these people:

- My darling E, who's been my inspiration and encouraged me throughout the creative process.
- My family, for their support and encouragement.
- Nick Saalfeld for his advice and help in developing my writing style.
- Emma Parkin and Joanna de Vries at Conker House publishing consultancy for their detailed manuscript analysis and editorial focus.
- Scott Addington for sharing his experiences as a published author and ongoing support.
- David Wood at London Futurists for his encouragement and running such high calibre learning events.
- The ModComms team including Rita, Hardi and James for their design and technical assistance.
- The Future Navigator team in Denmark for their fantastic training course that got me started.
- The BYC Yoga centre in Chiswick, London. Many of the ideas in the book crystallised after good sessions there.
- Paul Foley for not even bothering to feign interest in the endeavour, but being a friend throughout.

- For their contributions to the videos: Miguel Veiga-Pestana, Professor James Woudhuysen, Piers Thurston, Barry Flack, Maggie Stilwell, Liz Slade, Waverly Labs, Dr Peter van Dijken, Matthias Niessner, Laurent Haug, Keiichi Matsuda, Dr Trudy Barber.